LANDMARK COLLECTOR'S LIBRARY

Stationary Steam Engines of Great Britain
The National Photographic Collection
Volume 3.2: Lancashire

George Watkins

The Watkins Collection in the National Monuments Record

This comprises the photographs and notes George Watkins made during a lifetime of study of the stationary steam engine.

The Steam Engine Record is an annotated set of around 1500 mounted prints of steam engines which Watkins examined in the field between 1930 and 1980. His notebooks contain a record of additional sites for which no photographs were taken, or which comprise written historical notes.
In all almost 2000 entries were made in his notebooks.
There are also albums of prints arranged by engine type. A catalogue is available.

In addition there are files of notes and other records on all aspects of historical steam technology, the cataloguing of which is in progress.

The main areas of this part of the collection are:

Records of steam engine makers.

Collection of bound trade literature.

Classified collection of data files dealing with,
for example, textile mill engines, marine engines.

The collection can be inspected by appointment.
Copies of photographs and other documents are readily available.

Please contact:

NMR Enquiry & Research Services
National Monuments Record Centre
Kemble Drive
Swindon
Wilts
SN2 2GZ

STATIONARY STEAM ENGINES OF GREAT BRITAIN

THE NATIONAL PHOTOGRAPHIC COLLECTION

VOLUME 3.2: LANCASHIRE

George Watkins

Landmark Publishing

Published by

Ashbourne Hall, Cokayne Ave
Ashbourne, Derbyshire DE6 1EJ England
Tel: (01335) 347349 Fax: (01335) 347303
e-mail: landmark@clara.net
web site: www.landmarkpublishing.co.uk

ISBN 1 901522 57 1

© George Watkins

Print: MPG Ltd, Bodmin, Cornwall
Designed by: James Allsopp
Editor: A P Woolrich
Production: C L M Porter

Front cover: St Helens Waterworks, Eccleston Hill Pumping Station, Preston, SER 801
Back cover: Warwick Mill, Middleton, SER 1164
Page 3: Emerson Road Mill, Preston, SER 1185

CONTENTS

51. Oldham, Lees & Wrigley Ltd	SER 504	84
52. Oldham, Lees & Wrigley (No. 4 Mill)	SER 729b	88
53. Oldham, Park Bridge Ironworks	SER 722	88
54. Oldham, Abraham Stott & Co, Osborne Mill, Busk	SER 968b	88
55. Oldham, Abraham Stott & Co, Osborne Mill, Busk	SER 968a	92
56. Oldham, The United Mill Co., Chadderton	SER 709	92
57. Oldham, The United Mill Co., Chadderton	SER 709a	92
58. Oldham, Whittaker and Co.	SER 538	96
59. Openshaw, Manchester, Hampson, Wrigley & Co.	SER 895	96
60. Oswaldtwistle, Shaw & Co, Rhyddings Mill	SER 785	96
61. Padiham, G Green & Co., Green Lane Shed	SER 1159	100
62. Padiham, Padiham Waste Co.	SER 1187	100
63. Pemberton, Enfield Manufacturing Co.	SER 862	100
64. Prescot, St. Helens Waterworks, Eccleston Hill Pumping Station	SER 801	104
65. Preston, John Barnes & Sons, Waverley Park Shed	SER 906	104
66. Preston, Emerson Road Mill	SER 1185	104
67. Preston, Horrockses, Crewdson Ltd., Fishwick Mill	SER 1031	108
68. Radcliffe, Walker Allen & Co.	SER 1415	108
69. Radcliffe, The East Lancashire Paper Mill Co.	SER 1230	108
70. Radcliffe, Hardcastle & Co.	SER 1156a	112
71. Radcliffe, Hardcastle & Co.	SER 1156b	112
72. Radcliffe, A & J Hoyle Ltd., Park Street Shed	SER 1157	112
73. Radclife, John B. Lomax & Co.	SER 1414	116
74. Radcliffe, Mount Sion Bleachworks	SER 1417	116
75. Ramsbottom, J. Ashworth & Co., Wood Road Mill, Summerseat	SER 1057	116
76. Ramsbottom, Pemberton & Co., Peel Bridge Mills	SER 911	120
77. Rawtenstall, Clowes Mill, Bury Road	SER 103a	120
78. Rawtenstall, Clowes Mill, Bury Road	SER 103b	120
79. Rawtenstall, Hardman Bros., New Hall Hey Mill	SER 156	124
80. Reddish, Broadstone Mills Ltd	SER 643	124
81. Reddish, Thos. Houldsworth & Co, South Mill	SER 644	124
82. Reddish, Spur Doubling Co.	SER 645	128
83. Rishton, Britannia Mill Co., Spring Street	SER 907	128
84. Rishton, R. & T. Clayton, Bridgefield Mills	SER 908	128
85. Rochdale, Arkwright Mill	SER 899b	132
86. Rochdale, Crest Ring Mill	SER 594	132
87. Rochdale, Dale Mill	SER 899a	132
88. Rochdale, Ensor Mill Co., Castleton	SER 876a	136
89. Rochdale, Ensor Mill Co., Castleton, (No. 2 Mill)	SER 876b	136
90. Rochdale, Era Mill Co., Woodbine Street	SER 597	136
91. Rochdale, S. & A. Heywood, Quarry Mill, Whitworth Road	SER 1103	140
92. Rochdale, Highams Ltd., Sudden	SER 938	140
93. Rochdale, Moss Bridge Mill, Moss Bridge	SER 720	140
94. Rochdale, Moss Mill	SER 596	144
95. Rochdale, T. Normanton & Co., Atlas Spring Works, Moss Street	SER 831	144
96. Rochdale, Samuel O'Neill & Co, Castleton	SER 970	144
97. Rochdale, The Redcross Street Doubling Mill Co.	SER 593	148
98. Rochdale, Rochdale Steam Laundry, Manchester Road	SER 1184	148
99. Rochdale, Schofield, Ltd., Buckley Mill	SER 175	148
100. Rochdale, Sparth Mill Co.	SER 591	152
101. Rochdale, Standard Mill	SER 590	152
102. Rochdale, Stott & Co., Mellor Street Mill	SER 719	152
103. Rochdale, Victoria Mill Co., Woodbine Street	SER 760	156
104. Royton, Roy Mill Co.	SER 710	156
105. Royton, Royton Ring Mill	SER 1131	156
106. Salford, J. Eaton & Co.	SER 1199	160
107. Salford, Seedley Bleach Works, later Croft Laundry	SER 1141	160

1. Leigh, Mather Lane Mill Co. No.2. Mill   SER 637

Type:	Inverted vertical single tandem compound
Photo taken:	
Maker and Date:	J. & E Wood Ltd., Bolton, 1882
Cylinder/dimensions:	23in and 37in x 4ft 0in – Corliss valves
Hp: 800	*Rpm:* 80 *Psi:* 80
Service:	Cotton spinning – Rope drive.

No. 2. Mill was very unusual in that it was a cubical block, the power plant being separate, with glass-cased main rope drives entirely outside the mill block. The drives were all designed to operate at high speeds, the room shafting being hollow with the joining flanges forged solid with the shafts themselves, whilst the driving ropes ran at the highest speed in the mill, i.e. 7,000 feet per minute, whereas the normal speed was about 5,000 feet per minute. There were only thirteen ropes to transmit full power whereas usually one rope was used for every 50 hp transmitted. The flywheel was made especially strong to resist this, comprising a small cast iron wheel with a strong steel extending rim and tension bar to resist bursting. This was one of the very few mills fitted with an ejector condenser. Electric ring spinning superseded steam.

2. Leigh, Mill Lane Mill   SER 1051

Type:	Horizontal cross compound condensing
Photo taken:	1961
Maker and Date:	Yates & Thom, Blackburn, 1913
Cylinder/dimensions:	24in and 48in x 5ft 0in – Corliss valves
Hp: 1,500	*Rpm:* 75 *Psi:* 180
Service:	Cotton spinning. 33 rope drive from 24ft flywheel.

Mill Lane was built as a mule spinning plant, and ran so until motor-driven ring frames were installed in the 1960s. The photograph shows it with most of the ring frames installed and with only the preparation load still on the engine. The changeover was completed and the engine removed in the early 1960s. This and other mills later in the Combined English Mills group were converted to motor-driven ring spinning frames, but many were closed as the modern ring frames on shift work produced much more yarn.

3. Leigh, Parsonage Colliery   SER 1331

Type:	Horizontal double cylinder
Photo taken:	1968
Maker and Date:	W & J Galloway Ltd., Manchester, 1923
Cylinder/dimensions:	40in x 6ft 0in – Drop valves
Hp: ?	*Rpm:* 45 *Psi:* 160
Service:	Coal winding. Shafts 1,000 yards deep.
	Rope drum about 16ft diameter.

This colliery sinking was started about 1912, and probably completed by the Government during the First World War. The No.2 shaft (Markham's engine) was probably put in about 1921. It had been a very fine engine giving little trouble despite very heavy use. There were some 54 revolutions per wind for No.1, and No.2 wound from the same depth in 36 revolutions, in 68 seconds. The Galloway had a differential three bevel wheel gear box (which can be seen in the print) in each of the side valve drive shafts, for reversing.

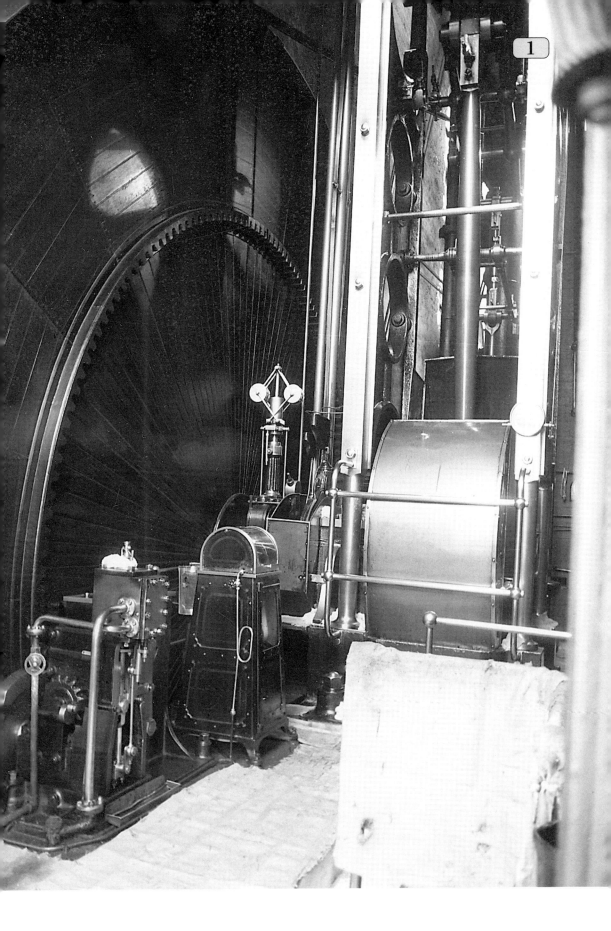

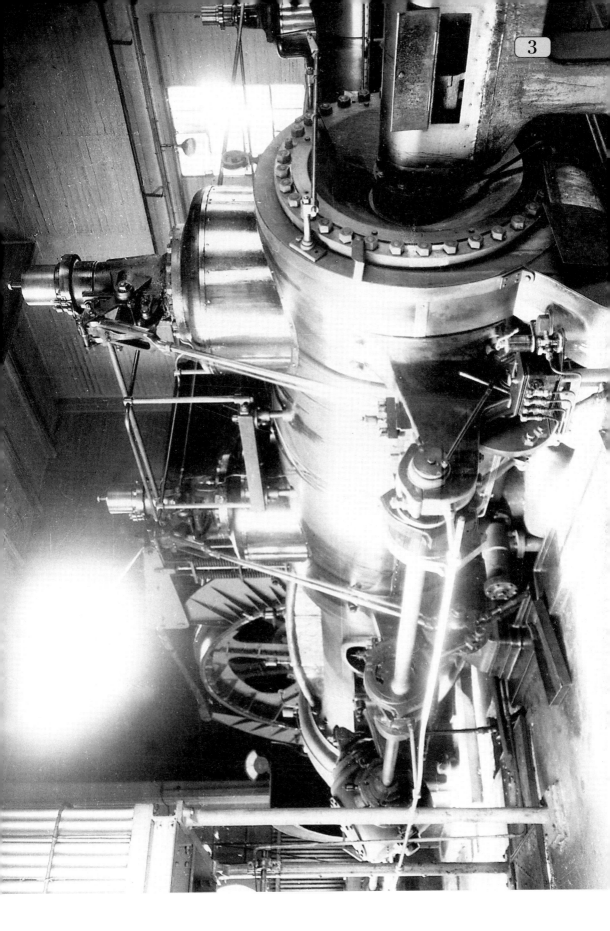

4. Leigh, Parsonage Colliery   SER 1180

Type:	Horizontal double cylinder
Photo taken:	1965
Maker and Date:	Galloways Ltd., Manchester, 1923
Cylinder/dimensions:	40in x 6ft 0in – Drop valves
Hp: ?	*Rpm:* 30 *Psi:* 140
Service:	Coal winding. Shaft 640 yards deep.
	Drum 16ft to 22ft diameter.

The only winding engine that Galloways made; it is a tribute to their design team and men, since it was very heavily used and gave little trouble generally. Reversing was by a three bevel wheel box in the layshaft driving the valves, which can just be seen at the extreme left of the print. By turning this through about 120 degrees, the phasing of the valve drive at the end was altered relative to the drive from the crankshaft. It was very simple and light to handle. The conico-cylindrical drum had four rising turns at the start to the parallel centre section, and the wind was completed in thirty revolutions and in about seconds. There was a Markham engine at No.2 pit, with a power station and ten boilers (1970).

5. Littleborough, Ebor Engineering Co.   SER 267

Type:	Single Cylinder Vertical
Photo taken:	1939
Maker and Date:	Sutcliffe & Co., Ebor Engineering Co., 1868
Cylinder/dimensions:	15in x 2ft 6in-Slide valve, non condensing
Hp:	*Psi:*
Service:	Works drive, shafts and belts

This was made in the works, probably soon after they started and was in regular use for nearly 70 years, until local electricity supplies were available. The simple rugged design served very well, as little had ever been done to the engine, except that the inevitable overloads had necessitated side stays to be attached to the supporting columns. A pleasing feature was that when the moulders had prepared for the casting of the columns, the moulding boxes were left open overnight, and the foundry cat walked upon one of them leaving the imprint of its foot. The moulders left this as its contribution to the works engine, and this together with *Sarah* and the date, made a link with either the wife or daughter of the works owner at the time.

6. Littleborough, Frankfort Mill   SER 104

Type:	Double McNaughted beam
Photo taken:	1935
Maker and Date:	Unknown, 1840?
Cylinder/dimensions:	Approx. 30in x 3ft 6in and 36in x 7ft 0in – Slide valves
Hp: Approx. 600	*Rpm:* Approx. 25 *Psi:* Approx. 80-100
Service:	Cotton spinning and weaving. Originally drove by two

pinions, one for the mill vertical shaft, the other for the weaving shed. Beams approx. 20ft long. Flywheel 18ft 0in diameter. Plant scrapped in 1936.

This was a plain substantial engine probably built in the 1840s, and McNaughted some 30 years later. An unusual feature was that the original slow speed governor, which was driven from the second motion shaft (i.e. not directly off the engine) remained in use until the end, although by then the original working pressure had been raised from about 20 to 80 psi or over. The drives were later altered so that the bottom mill floor and the weaving shed were then driven by a 30in belt from the second motion, instead of gearing, but the drive was still taken from the two flywheel pinions.

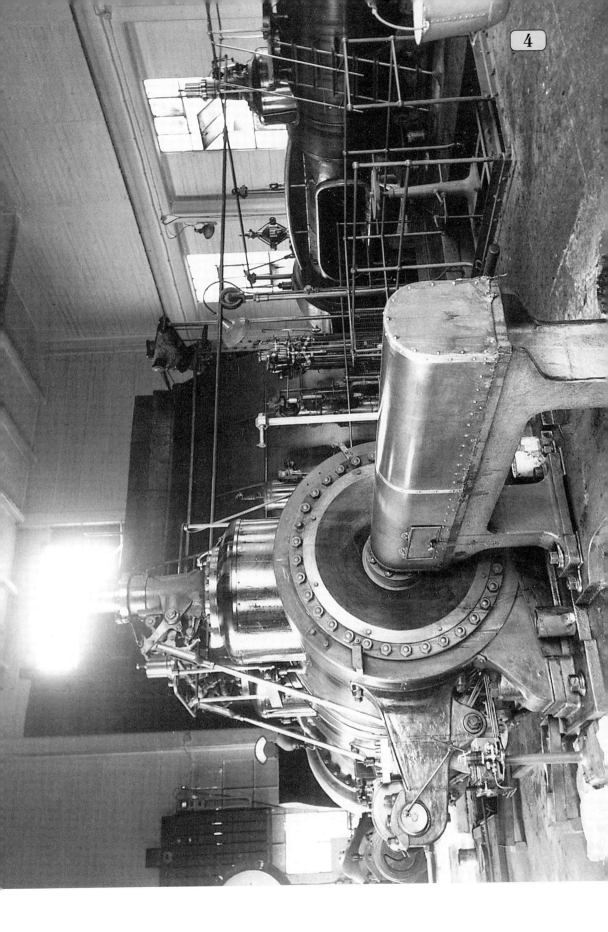

7. Littleborough, A & W Law Ltd., Lydgate   SER 174

Type:	Single cylinder vertical non-condensing
Photo taken:	1936
Maker and Date:	Probably Ebor Engineering Co., Date unknown.
Cylinder/dimensions:	15in x 2ft 6in
Hp: ?	*Psi:*
Service:	Mill drive to assist turbine (was water wheel).

A very plain engine of late design, whose history was unknown, this had to work far longer after the water turbine was installed. The water feed to the wheel could be adjusted to that available, whilst the turbine rapidly drained the pond in low water periods, since the efficiency fell off very rapidly if the turbine was throttled down to run to use the reduced flow

8. Liverpool Waterworks, Aubrey Street Pumping Station   SER 759

Type:	Vertical triple expansion	
Photo taken:	1955	
Maker and Date:	Hathorn, Davey & Co., Sun Foundry, Leeds, 1896	
Cylinder/dimensions:	15in, 28in and 38in x 3ft 0in	
Hp: 179	*Rpm: 34*	*Psi: 140*
Service:	Pumped filtered water to high level areas. 300,000 gallons per hour.	

This unusual but very compact design had the 3 ram pumps below the engine, driven by piston tail rods, each plunger or ram being 22in diameter. It was Hathorn, Davey's standard triple expansion type with the engine inverted, providing a lightly stressed engine in a small house. It was little used in the 1950s, and was believed to have been scrapped soon after. The contract price for the engine and the pumps installed was £3,800 in 1896.

9. Liverpool Waterworks, Dudlow Lane Pumping Station   SER 100a

Type:	Cornish beam *Thos. Duncan*	
Photo taken:	1935	
Maker and Date:	Rothwell & Co., Union Foundry, Bolton, 1869	
Cylinder/dimensions:	56in x 10ft 0in ?	
Hp: ?	*Rpm: 8-10*	*Psi: 60*
Service:	Town supply from wells. 2 bucket pumps in well 230ft down with 180ft surface lift to water tower. Beam 32ft 0in long. Scrapped 1947.	

A good example of Lancashire workmanship in the Cornish tradition. The whole was very well finished, and the 'Liver' bird cast on the entablature together with the decoration of the top of the columns were individual pieces of civic pride.

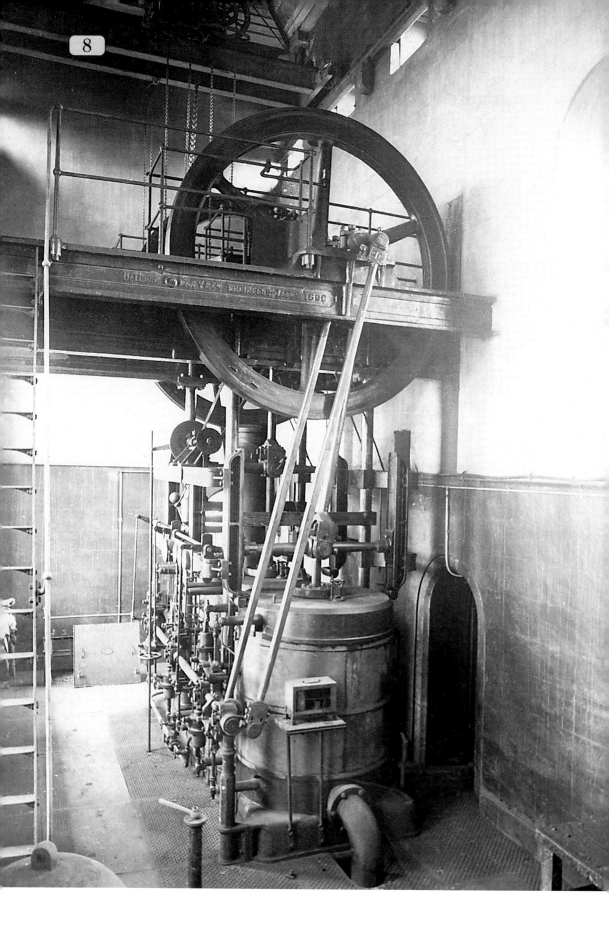

10. *Liverpool Waterworks, Green Lane Pumping Station*   SER 99a

Type:	Cornish beam
Photo taken:	1935
Maker and Date:	Harvey & Co., Hayle, 1845
Cylinder/dimensions:	50in x 9ft 0in
Hp: 69	*Rpm:* 8-10 *Psi:* 40
Service:	City supply from wells to reservoir.

Called *Holmes* this was a standard Cornish engine, which pumped 83 gallons per stroke. The well and surface lift pumps were in line, with the surface set on girders, straddled by the side rods which went down to the well pumps. The total head was about 300ft, the engine pumping over a standpipe for safety. All of the steam plant was replaced after 1950.

11. *Liverpool Waterworks, Green Lane Pumping Station*   SER 99b

Type:	Cornish beam
Photo taken:	1935
Maker and Date:	G. Forrester, Vauxhall Foundry, Liverpool, 1851
Cylinder/dimensions:	52in x 9ft 0in
Hp:	*Rpm:* *Psi:*
Service:	City supply wells to reservoir, 3,500,000 gallons per day. 300ft head.

Called *George Holt*, this pumped 104 gallons per stroke. The twin fluted columns were a contrast to the four plain ones of 99a, otherwise the two engines had much in common. This engine together with its boilers cost £5,750, all being scrapped in the re-organisation after 1950. An interesting feature of these two engines, which were in adjacent houses, was that the wells were at the opposite ends of the houses.

12. *Liverpool Waterworks, Green Lane Pumping Station*   SER 99c

Type:	Rotative beam
Photo taken:	1935
Maker and Date:	Mather Dixon, 1837
Cylinder/dimensions:	34$\frac{1}{2}$ in x 6ft 1in
Hp:	*Rpm:* *Psi:*
Service:	City supply.

Called *J. Cooper* this was installed at Bootle originally, and removed to Green Lane, in 1856. It was unaltered, retaining the lattice eccentric rod, ornate valve chest, and massive connecting rod, all being scrapped with the other engines.

13. Longridge, nr. Preston, Smith Bros., Victoria Mill, Berry Lane SER 826a

Type:	Horizontal single tandem
Photo taken:	1956
Maker and Date:	Ashton, Frost and Co., Blackburn, 1903?
Cylinder/dimensions:	16in and 30in x 3ft 0in – Corliss and slide valves
Hp: 350	*Rpm:* 90 *Psi:* 120
Service:	Cotton weaving.

The mill was driven by a beam engine (possibly by Hick, Hargreaves, Bolton) through gearing until 1938, this using about 20 tons of coal per week to develop 400 hp. The present tandem engine was then purchased secondhand from a closed mill, and this, driving by ropes, used about half of the fuel. The mill continued to run reasonably until trade fell off and the mill was closed about 1960, when all was scrapped. This example was typical of the engines, sturdy simple and economical which Ashton, Frost supplied to many small plants, but which have now disappeared. The only addition was the electric stop motion giving instant stopping from the mill rooms by push buttons.

14. Lostock Junction, Bolton, Wm. Heaton & Sons SER 1092

Type:	Horizontal cross compound
Photo taken:	1962
Maker and Date:	John Musgrave & Sons Ltd., Bolton, 1907
Cylinder/dimensions:	21^1/$_2$ in and 43in x 4ft 0in – Corliss valves
Hp: 800	*Rpm:* 73 *Psi:* 160
Service:	Cotton spinning. 30 rope drive to alternator. No. 1 Mill.

The mill was built in 1856, and was powered by a beam engine made by Knight and Wood, Bolton. This ran with geared drives until replacement was needed due to wear and increasing load. This engine was then installed, at first driving by ropes to the original room shafts, and when later the drives were turned over to motors this engine was rearranged to drive the alternator in the basement by 23 ropes from the flywheel. This can be seen in the photograph, where the ropes all follow the same path to the single pulley, instead of to the several floors as it was before. There were two mills, the other with a similar engine later converted to triple expansion. The mills were closed about 1960, when all was scrapped, including 5 boilers installed new in 1922.

15. Manchester, Bradford Colliery SER 647

Type:	Vertical twin cylinder non-condensing
Photo taken:	1954
Maker and Date:	Robert Daglish & Co., St. Helens, 1904
Cylinder/dimensions:	42in x 6ft 0in – Drop valves
Hp: ?	*Rpm:* up to 30 *Psi:* 120
Service:	Coal winding. 3,500ft deep.

This was one of the deepest collieries in the U.K. A very costly electrical conversion scheme, with tower winders, and motors designed to work efficiently from three depths was completed about 1968, and all steam scrapped. It was then decided that the risk of subsidence to the many tall buildings in the area was too great and it was decided to close the colliery completely. The site was being cleared in 1972.

16. Manchester, Thomas Guest & Co.   SER 496

Type:	Single cylinder non-condensing
Photo taken:	1952
Maker and Date:	George Saxon Ltd., Manchester, 1860s?
Cylinder/dimensions:	15in x 2ft 0in – Slide valve
Hp: 60	*Rpm:* 90 *Psi:* 100
Service:	Confectioners; toffee manufactory drive.

There was no positive evidence about the maker of this engine, but it was similar to Saxon's early design and they had always maintained it. Very plain, it was economical and fitted with a Meyer variable cut-off valve. There were 5 floors in the works, driven by 3 ropes from the flywheel, to mainshafts on 3 floors, and ropes from two of these to the other floors. The works closed in the 1960s, possibly due to redevelopment.

17. Manchester, The Holt Town Refuse Destructor Depot, Ancoats
SER 495

Type:	Horizontal single cylinder condensing
Photo taken:	1952
Maker and Date:	W & J Galloway, Manchester. 1870s
Cylinder/dimensions:	22in bore for two and 28in other two 3ft 0in
Hp: 30 & 50	*Rpm:* 60 *Psi:* 10-20
Service:	Plant drives

These engines powered the dry sewage and refuse disposal system of the district, the garbage being incinerated for manure etc., prior to the installation of the water borne sewage system and then for refuse destruction only. They were plain engines that gave little trouble and were named after council members – *Goldschmidt* and *Schofield* for the larger and *Shaw* and *Brown* for the smaller ones. The drives were by cotton ropes to the works shafting and the whole was well kept.

18. Manchester, Jackson Street Spinning Co.   SER 470

Type:	Horizontal cross compound condensing
Photo taken:	1952
Maker and Date:	J. & E. Wood Ltd., Bolton, 1870, compounded, 1899
Cylinder/dimensions:	27in and 51in x 5ft 0in – Corliss valves
Hp: 1,500	*Rpm:* 52 *Psi:* 160
Service:	Cotton spinning. Fine counts.

This was probably built as a twin cylinder slide valve engine, as Woods did not take up Corliss valves extensively until 1871-2. There was a serious fire in the later 1890s, possibly 1900, as Scott & Hodgson supplied the new flywheels and gear in 1900, and the engine may have been moved to give extra room for the rope drive. J.& E. Wood supplied the new cylinders which ran until the mill closed and the premises were merged into Manchester University in the 1960s. The drive was by a gearwheel of 13ft 6in diameter (which was placed between the 18ft flywheels) and second motion shaft to the rope driving pulley. The yarn spun was some of the finest in the trade i.e. 200s if needed.

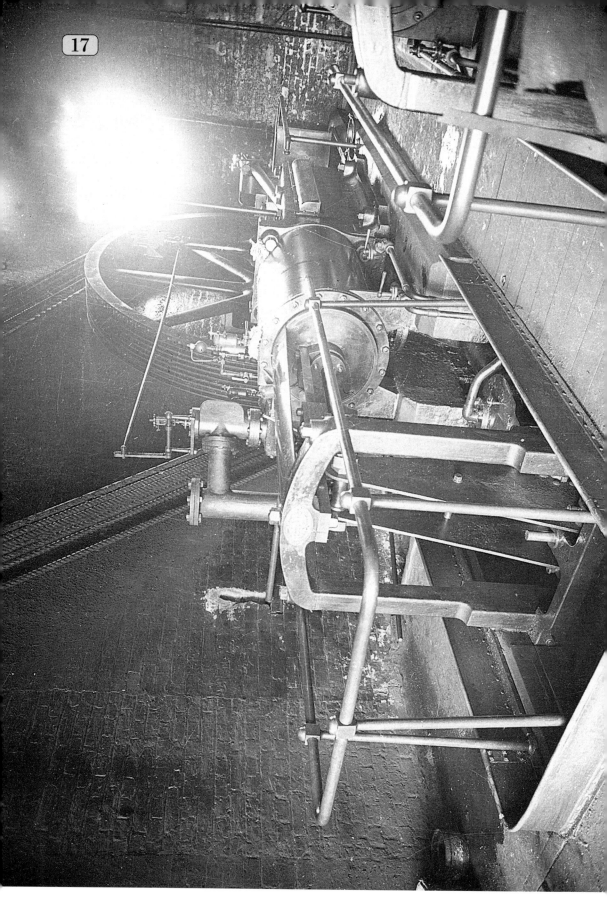

19. Manchester, David Moseley & Co., Rubber Works, Ardwick
SER 361

Type:	Horizontal single tandem condensing
Photo taken:	1950
Maker and Date:	Pollit & Wigzell, Sowerby Bridge c.1890s – No. 260
Cylinder/dimensions:	13in and 24½ in x 3ft 6in – Corliss and slide valves
Hp: 200	*R.p.m:* 80　　　　*Psi:* 100
Service:	Mill drive

From being entirely steam engine driven in the 1930s, Moseleys had turned to electric drives by the 1950s and this was the last of five or six engines they once used. It was a standard Pollit engine, with the condenser arranged beside the crank to save space lengthwise. It drove two lines of rubber calendering mills by the gearing at the right and was under overhaul during the holiday shut down when photographed, the condenser back cover is seen by the wall at the left. The business closed in 1971.

20. Manchester, Peel, Williams & Peel, Pollard Street, Ancoats SER 849b

Type:	Engineers' workshops

The works occupied an area of the whole of the buildings seen, plus a large yard behind with a foundry and other buildings. The gear wheels on the top were an unusual decoration even for a shop which made many hundreds a year for half a century. Another interesting feature was the works clock on the other side of the yard, i.e. again at the top of the building. This was also framed by a gear wheel motif; this time a bevel wheel. The simple moulded pilasters are typical of Fairbairn's early attempts to make the functional structures more attractive. All were demolished later.

21. Manchester, Pollock & Co., Harding St., Ancoats　　　SER 1339

Type:	Pipe maker's bench

This factory was very old-established, and made a very wide range of pipes for export to many countries. Large numbers went to Africa, and the East, and the range of the moulds was great since every design had its own mould. Pipes with highly decorated bowls, others with raised motifs on the stems, such as those in the foreground, and large numbers of the long stemmed churchwardens were made. There was a single gas fired kiln with 10 operatives. Plastic clay was essential, as air bubbles would expand and spoil in firing and a stiff clay would not accurately follow the moulds, some of which were very complex such as those for the Order of Buffaloes. The whole process can be seen. The operator sat at the left with the finished pipes on the right, and the process was to take one of the flattened blanks seen in front, and place it in the split mould (which was slightly smeared with grease from the plate at the right) seen in front of the seat. The split mould was then folded together and placed in the moulding frame at the left, held by screwing in the clamp screw. The moulding was done by pulling down the lever which contained a metal pin, to mould the bowl, and as this made the bowl, it compressed the rest of the clay into the mould, making a complete blank pipe seen ready for the kiln on the right. The site was to be cleared in 1968 threatening the future of the works.

22. Middleton, Cromer Ring Spinning Mill   SER 858

Type:	Inverted vertical triple expansion
Photo taken:	1957
Maker and Date:	Buckley & Taylor, Oldham, 1904
Cylinder/dimensions:	25in, 34in and 52in x 4ft 0in – Corliss valves
Hp: 2,000	*Rpm:* 75 *Psi:* 200
Service:	Cotton spinning. 34 rope drive.

This was typical of the later designs which were adopted after the turn of the 19th century to drive the mills of the last great expansion of English mill building. The mill itself however was by no means typical since it comprised a single floor only, whereas four or more floors were standard. Blessed by very sound management, the mill was always busy, to which all contributed. The engine was always fully loaded, and in 1925 the original high pressure cylinder of $22\frac{1}{2}$ in bore had to be replaced by that noted above, as the load was running up to 2,400 hp. It ran thus until the whole of the load was put to electrical drives in the early 1960s, when the engine was scrapped; the mill still ran successfully in the 1970s.

23. Middleton, Warwick Mill   SER 1164

Type:	Horizontal cross compound
Photo taken:	1964
Maker and Date:	George Saxon Ltd., Manchester, 1909
Cylinder/dimensions:	$25\frac{1}{4}$ in and 52in x 5ft 0in – Corliss valves
Hp: 1,500	*Rpm:* 65 *Psi:* 180
Service:	Cotton spinning. 30 rope drive off 26ft flywheel.

This was a standard Saxon engine, which was designed for and always ran with steam superheated to 500°F. There were four Tinker, Shenton boilers, which were still insured for the original pressure of 180 psi. The tubular tail rod cases were interesting, and had the engines' name plates *Hannah* and *Mary* mounted upon them. Warwick also was one of the few engines which Saxon built with an air pump on either side although there was only one condenser. Warwick was a good mill which kept the engine well loaded for much of its life, and the mill continued cotton spinning with motor drives after the mid-1960s. The engine was scrapped.

24. Miles Platting, Manchester, Wm. Holland Co, Victoria Mill   SER 713

Type:	Two vertical compound.
Photo taken:	1955
Maker and Date:	John Musgrave & Sons, Bolton, 1902
Cylinder/dimensions:	$26\frac{1}{2}$ in and 50in x 3ft 6in
Hp: 1000	*Rpm:* 75 *Psi:* 160
Service:	Fine cotton spinning

Musgraves made this design under licence from Fleming and Ferguson of Paisley. These were installed in a rebuild after a serious fire which damaged the double beam engine and vertical shafts in use to 1902. It was a large mill, with a fine chimney and with four boilers on the canal side at the back. It was unable to keep running when the fine yarn demand fell off, and the very sound plant was all scrapped.

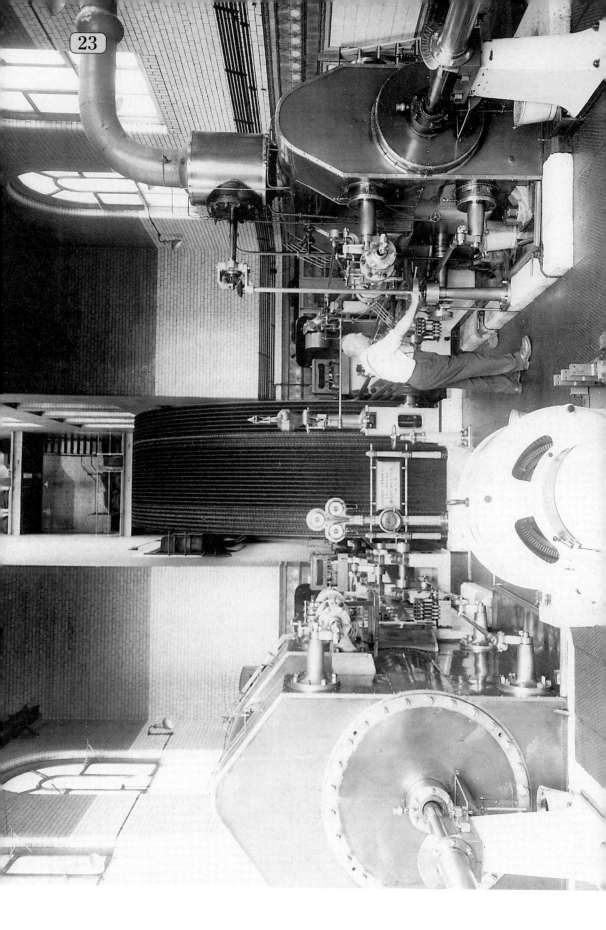

25. Milnrow, Richard Barnes & Co., Firgrove Mill   SER 1030

Type:	Horizontal single tandem condensing
Photo taken:	1960
Maker and Date:	J. & W. McNaught, St. George's Foundry, Rochdale 1907
Cylinder/dimensions:	15³/₄ in and 31¹/₂ in x 4ft 0in – Corliss and slide valves
Hp: 500	*Rpm:* 78 *Psi:* 160
Service:	Woollens, blankets etc. 9 rope drive to mill and weaving shed.

Firgrove was an old established mill, which had been driven by a beam engine until 1907, when this engine of greater power was installed on additions being made to the mill and plant. The low pressure cylinder was fitted with a Meyer type slide valve and the high pressure with the later McNaught Corliss type valve. There was a single Lancashire boiler by Hewitt and Kellett of Bradford, which being of 1916 date means that the engine ran with the beam engine boiler for some nine years. The mill was converted to electrical driving later and the engine was moved to the Manchester Museum store for eventual re-erection. The mill was finally closed about three years after conversion to motor drive was completed.

26. Monton, nr. Manchester, The Monton Mill Co.   SER 1005

Type:	Inverted vertical cross compound
Photo taken:	1959
Maker and Date:	George Saxon Ltd., Manchester
Cylinder/dimensions:	27in and 56in x 4ft 0in – Corliss valves
Hp: 1,200	*Rpm:* 75 *Psi:* 180
Service:	Cotton spinning. 30 rope drive to mill shafts, off 22ft flywheel.

This was Saxon's usual design, with very little alteration except for the fitting of a Lumb governor. It was a good mill which was always busy and well loaded. There were three Oldham Ironworks Co., boilers which were still insured for the original 180 psi in the 1960s when the drives were converted to electric motors. It was made more economical by the fitting of superheaters, possibly in the 1920s, and these slightly increased the wear, but it was very good plant which paid well. The flywheel was about 22ft diameter, and the cranks were plain steel forgings shrunk onto the shaft. It was probably the last Saxon vertical compound at work.

27. Mossley, The Carr Hill Mill Co.   SER 631

Type:	Horizontal four cylinder triple expansion
Photo taken:	1954
Maker and Date:	J. Petrie & Co., Rochdale
Cylinder/dimensions:	20in, 32in, 36in and 36in x 5ft 0in
Hp: 1,400	*Rpm:* 60 *Psi:* 160
Service:	Cotton spinning. Rope drive.

This engine was possibly bought second-hand from another mill; no positive history was known, but Petries' engines were rarely installed new in the Mossley area. It remained literally as it was built, except for the addition of a Lumb governing system. All of the machinery was scrapped when the mill was closed in the poor trade of the 1950s.

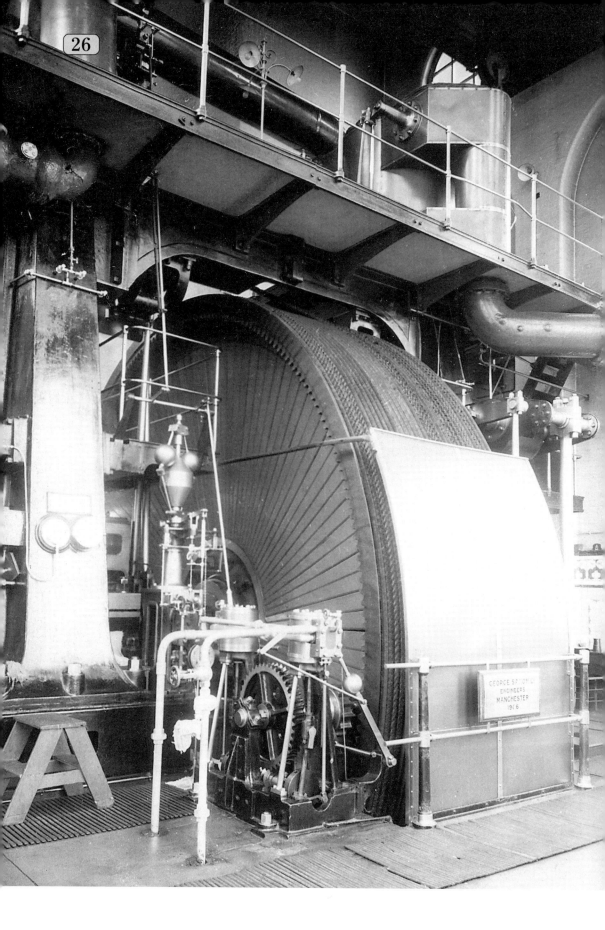

GEORGE SAXON L
ENGINEERS
MANCHESTER
1906

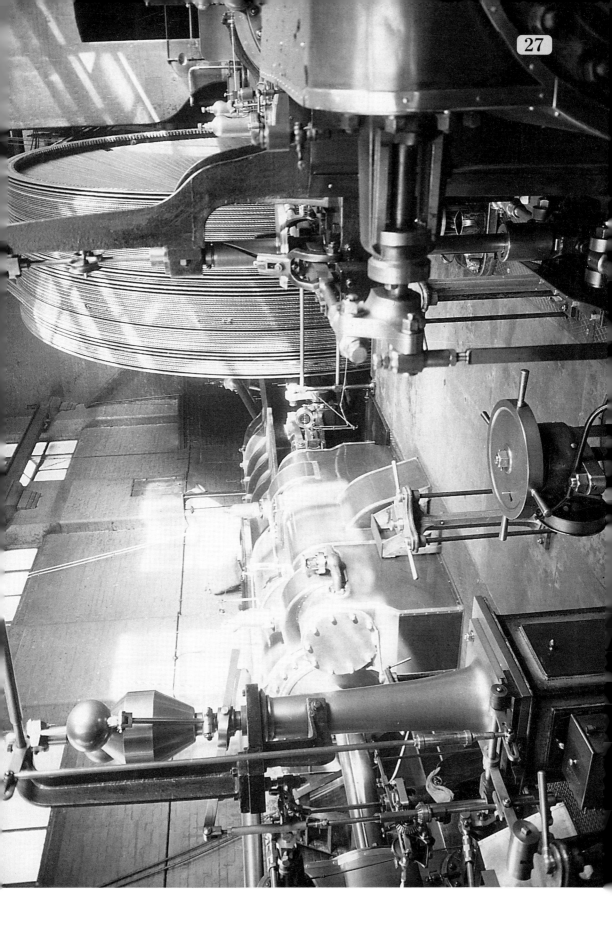

28. Nelson, The Marsden Mill Co., Brunswick Road — SER 916a

Type:	Horizontal cross compound
Photo taken:	1958
Maker and Date:	Burnley Ironworks Co., 1908
Cylinder/dimensions:	20in and 40in x 4ft 0in – Corliss valves
Hp: 800	*Rpm:* 84 *Psi:* 160
Service:	Cotton weaving. 18 rope drive. No. 1 shed.

Marsden was one of the latest weaving concerns to start, and was really large, having some 2,000 looms at one time, in two large stone-built sheds, each with its own engine and with the three boilers in a house between them. Both engines were typical Burnley Ironworks designs but the later one had all of the valves below the cylinders, a design which they had introduced early in the 1900s. It ran well loaded at times, with little more than routine repairs, but the poor trade of the 1950s caused the closure of first one shed which was sold, the other following in the mid 1960s, when all of the remaining plant was scrapped. The neat circular condenser, and the high-speed governor, and generally neat finish were typical of the later Burnley engines.

29. Nelson, Pendle St Room & Power Co., — SER 977

Type:	Horizontal cross compound
Photo taken:	1959
Maker and Date:	Wm Roberts and Co., Nelson, c. 1888
Cylinder/dimensions:	23in and 46in x 5ft 0in – Corliss valves
Hp: 1000	*Rpm:* 45 *Psi:* 160
Service:	Cotton weaving. Geared drive.

This was always a room and power plant with the engine (originally having the Roberts standard slide valve cylinders design (see no. 1055). At times it was driving well over 2,000 narrow looms, but later the shed had 1,300 wide looms. The boilers were worn, and more power was needed in 1923, when possibly the change was made to wide looms which took much more power, and new Corliss valve cylinders by Roberts, together with three new boilers were installed. It will be seen that the Corliss valve gear is on the outer side of the high pressure cylinder, where the slide valve was in the original layout. Superheaters were added with the new boilers and the whole was very economical until the drives were changed over to electric motors in 1969, when the engine was scrapped. The gearing would be wearing after some 70 years of heavy duty in any case.

30. Nelson, The Seedhill Mill Co. — SER 976

Type:	Horizontal cross compound
Photo taken:	1959
Maker and Date:	Wm. Roberts & Co., Phoenix Foundry, Nelson, 1885?
Cylinder/dimensions:	17$^1/_8$ in and 35$^1/_8$ in x 4ft 0in – Corliss and slide valves
Hp: 500	*Rpm:* 45 *Psi:* 150
Service:	Cotton weaving. 27in belt drive.

The history was uncertain, but this was probably originally built with slide valves on the high pressure cylinder and fitted with a new Corliss valve cylinder and boiler about 1910. It was very quiet and drove from the 19ft flywheel to a 10ft 6in pulley on the shed mainshaft. The low pressure and engine motion were certainly unaltered, but the governor may have been modified. The boiler, installed in 1910, was condemned in 1957 and replaced by one by Yates and Thom, but the mill closed and all was scrapped in the 1960s. It was typical of Roberts's engines when modernised, as many were in the early 1900s.

31. Nelson, Spring Bank Mill — SER 169a

Type:	Quadruple expansion vertical non dead centre
Photo taken:	1936
Maker and Date:	John Musgrave & Sons, Bolton, 1892
Cylinder/dimensions:	13½in, 18½in, 26in and 37in x 3ft 6in stroke – Corliss valves

Hp: 650   *Rpm:* 80   *Psi:* 200

Service: Cotton weaving. 13 rope drive to shed mainshaft.

This was the standard Fleming & Ferguson non-dead-centre design which Musgraves built under licence from 1891 to 1907. It always ran well, but was soon overloaded, and in 1916 was carrying 800 hp, the maximum it could take, and it continued to develop well over 700 hp. A new hp cylinder was supplied by Roberts 1928, and was rebored twice by 1962. Always on overtime, it ran for some years for 16 hours per day. Three boilers built by Fernihoughs were working at 200 psi in 1963 after 70 years of work.

32. Nelson, Spring Bank Mill — SER 169b

Type:	Quadruple expansion engine
Photo taken:	
Maker and Date:	
Cylinder/dimensions:	

Hp: *Rpm:*   *Psi:*

Service:

The two piston rods of the non-dead-centre engine were coupled together by a cast steel triangular connecting rod. It was inverted, with the apex at the crankpin, and with a guiding link at the centre of the top member. Although self starting at almost every point, there was one angle at which it would not get away comfortably.

33. Nelson, Vale Street Room and Power Co. — SER 704a

Type:	Horizontal cross compound condensing
Photo taken:	1955
Maker and Date:	Wm. Roberts & Co., Phoenix Foundry, Nelson, 1890
Cylinder/dimensions:	19in and 38in x 5ft 0in – Corliss valves

Hp: 650   *Rpm:* 56   *Psi:* 140

Service: Supplied power and shed space for small groups of weavers. Gear drive. No. 1 shed.

Room and power service was popular among weavers who could rent room and power and purchase their own looms, which in the late 19th century could be bought for £16.00 each. In this way they were with small capital, enabled to start up in business. Many such starts developed into substantial concerns later owning their own sheds. The Vale Street Co., was a large example of this which later developed so that two engines were needed. No.1 was built as a standard Roberts's design engine fitted with slide valves, and the Corliss valve cylinders were fitted in 1924 when less power was required, and higher pressure boilers had been installed.

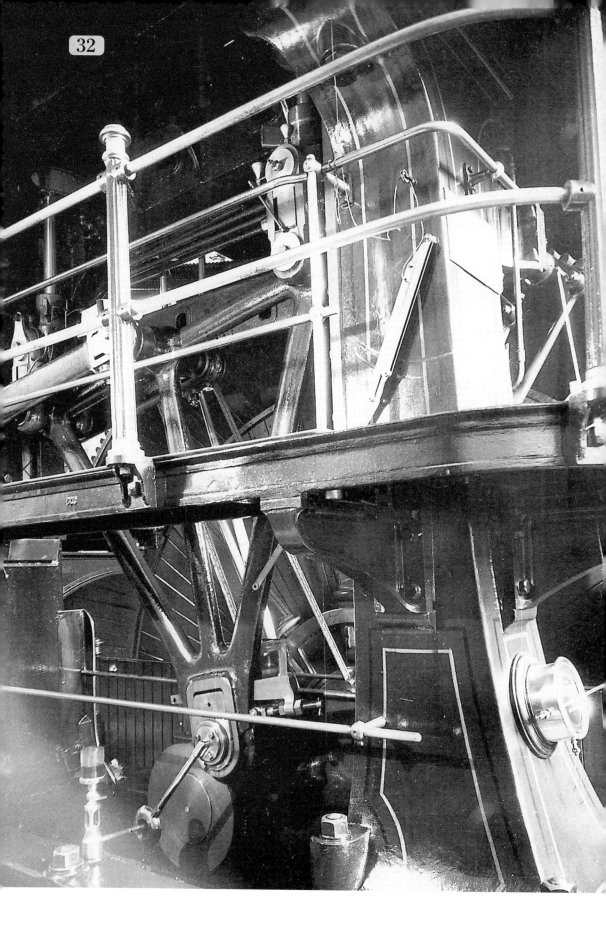

34. Nelson, Vale Street Room and Power Co. SER 704b

Type:	Inverted vertical cross compound
Photo taken:	1955
Maker and Date:	Wm. Roberts & Co., Phoenix Foundry, Nelson, 1906?
Cylinder/dimensions:	17in and 30in x 3ft 0in – Corliss and slide valves
Hp: 500	*Rpm:* 75 *Psi:* 140
Service:	As 704a but rope drive. No. 2 shed.

When, following the diversion of a river, the shed was extended in 1906, rope drives were widely used for weaving shed main drives. No.2 was so arranged, and the necessary length for the ropes was gained by adopting a vertical engine. The shed was now over 500ft long and the continuous mainshaft was made for easy coupling, so that the two engines could be coupled to drive the long shaft, for the 2,500 looms which could now be installed. This was done for some twenty five years, but later as trade fell off, the vertical engine was disconnected, and No.1 run alone. The greatly increased import of cheap foreign material severely affected trade and the shed was closed in 1963, when all was scrapped. The great length of the shed was, however, outstanding even in the heart of the Colne weaving district.

35. Nelson, The Victoria Mill Co. SER 804

Type:	Inverted vertical two crank triple expansion
Photo taken:	1956
Maker and Date:	Unknown
Cylinder/dimensions:	9in /16in and 26in x 3ft 0in – Corliss and slide valves
Hp: 300?	*Rpm:* 80 *Psi:* 140
Service:	Cotton weaving.

The engine was built as a slide valve compound to replace a beam engine, and it was probably made by Joseph Thompson who had an engineers' shop in Colne from 1880 onwards. It was very plain but substantial, with little to go wrong. More power and higher economy was required in the early 1900s, when weaving was expanding rapidly in the area, and a new boiler was installed for higher pressure, and the engine made triple expansion by adding a Corliss valve cylinder on top of the existing high pressure slide valve one. This work was also done by Thompson, and the engine gave little trouble until the business was closed in the late 1950s. It was probably the last surviving example of his work.

36. Nelson, The Whitefield Mill Co., Victoria Street SER 917

Type:	Horizontal cross compound
Photo taken:	1958
Maker and Date:	W. & J. Yates, Blackburn, 1880
Cylinder/dimensions:	24in and 49in x 5ft 0in – Slide then Corliss valves
Hp: 1,000	*Rpm:* 56 *Psi:* 160
Service:	Room and power service for small groups of weavers. Gear drive.

The business was started in 1880 with a Yates slide valve engine, driving two sheds from a single mainshaft between them, driving 18 loom cross shafts on either side, and with 5 more in one shed, to drive some 2,000 looms. The engine ran with the original boilers at 100 psi until 1926, when with the plant heavily overloaded, new Corliss valve cylinders and three boilers were installed by Yates & Thom of Blackburn. The gearing and drives were massive enough to take the higher power of the new layout (some 200 hp more) and the plant ran very satisfactorily and with good economy into the 1960s, but probably closed about 1963-4? It was a typical Yates's engine in all respects and the new cylinders were equally characteristic of Yates and Thom with very neat cast iron covers, Dobson Corliss gear, and the high speed governor.

37. New Hey, nr Rochdale, Ellenroad Ring Mill   SER 599

Type:	Built as a four cylinder triple, converted to compound in 1921
Photo taken:	1953
Maker and Date:	J. & W. McNaught, St. George's Foundry, Rochdale, 1892 [G. W. quotes 1910]
Cylinder/dimensions:	Later 23in and 44in x 6ft 0in – Corliss and piston valves.
Hp: Approx. 2,500	*Rpm:* 65 *Psi:* 180
Service:	Cotton spinning. Flywheel 28ft diameter. 44 ropes.

Ellenroad was large by any standard, and was equipped with 121,850 mule spindles when built. Most of the mill was destroyed in a fire in 1921, and it was rebuilt for ring spinning. This only needed two instead of the original four floors for the same production, but also required some 25% more power. The engine was therefore rebuilt by Clayton, Goodfellow of Blackburn, as a double compound, retaining the original five Yates and Thom boilers. Conversion of the mill to electric ring frames proceeded gradually, and by 1971 the load was down to 900 hp, and only one side of the engine was used. This load was still on the engine, which was the last but one of the large spinning mill engines to remain at work, in 1972.

38. New Hey nr Rochdale, The Garfield Mill Co.   SER 973

Type:	Horizontal twin tandem, later triple expansion.
Photo taken:	1959
Maker and Date:	J. Petrie & Co., Rochdale,1883. John Musgrave & Sons Ltd., Bolton, 1902
Cylinder/dimensions:	$24^3/_4$ in/36in and 2 x 40in x 5 ft 0 in – Corliss and piston valves
Hp: Approx. 1,4000	*Rpm:* 65 *Psi:* 160
Service:	Cotton spinning. 26 rope drive off 27ft flywheel.

This was built new in 1883 as a standard Petrie's piston valve twin tandem compound and converted to triple expansion twenty years later by Musgrave, as far as could be traced. Certainly it had been altered by Musgrave and was certainly of Petries' make, originally. The twist motion on the low pressure piston valves was disused later, otherwise little but the original high pressure cylinders was altered until the mill closed about 1963 when all was scrapped and later, the mill buildings were also demolished. The Corliss valve gear was driven by inclined shaft to a cross shaft between the front and rear cylinders which was beneath the round ended oiling boxes in line across the floor.

39. New Hey, nr Rochdale, Greenhalgh & Co.   SER 1287

Type:	Double diagonal twin cylinder
Photo taken:	1967
Maker and Date:	Pickup & Knowles, Pendleton, 1890s
Cylinder/dimensions:	7in x 1ft 0in – Slide valve
Hp: 12	*Rpm:* 70 *Psi:* 80

Another standard textile "donkey engine", this was massively built and very simple. The main frame comprised a single large casting at each side, with the crosshead guides upon a casting which bridged the frames. The machines were electrically driven as were the rest of the works, but this was retained as standby, it was probably later donated to the Northern Mill Engine Society. It was a typical steam work horse which thrived as so many did, on neglect.

40. New Hey, nr Rochdale, R Howarth & Co, Jubilee Mill   SER 1287b

Type:	Horizontal single cylinder non condensing
Photo taken:	1967
Maker and Date:	Ebor Engineering Co., Littleborough, 1891
Cylinder/dimensions:	16 in x 2ft 6in – Slide valve
Hp: 40	*Rpm:* 80 *Psi:* 90
Service:	Works drive. 12in belt to main shaft from 8 ft flywheel to 5 ft pulley. Textile finishers.

This was in use for over three quarters of a century, and was unaltered, except possibly for the fitting of metallic packing to the piston rod. It was almost certainly overloaded at times, few textile engines were not, and this appeared to have been in a house built for it, and survived a recent bad fire. It was, however, broken up later, with the full electrical driving of the plant. It was almost certainly the last Ebor-made engine left – they were millwrights rather than engine builders – and was named *Alice*.

41. Norden, nr Rochdale, R Cudworth   SER 965b

Type:	Horizontal single tandem condensing
Photo taken:	1959
Maker and Date:	S.S. Stott & Co., Laneside Foundry, Haslingden, 1895
Cylinder/dimensions:	Approx. 12in and 24in x 2ft 6in – Corliss and slide valves.
Hp: 150	*Rpm:* 100 *Psi:* 140
Service:	Weaving shed drive by ropes. Cotton manufacturers.

The mill was old established and this replaced a beam engine, which was still single cylinder in 1894. A tender to McNaught compound the beam for about £160 was made but it was wisely decided to install a new engine, which was still running in 1972, having given very little trouble. It was a standard Stott's engine in all ways: simple, sturdy and reliable. Electrical drives were installed in 1973.

42. Oldham, Belgrave Spinning Co, Hathershaw   SER 967

Type:	Horizontal cross compounding condensing
Photo taken:	1959
Maker and Date:	Urmson & Thompson, Oldham. 1906
Cylinder/dimensions:	26in and 56in x 5ft 0in – Corliss Valves
Hp: 1800	*Rpm:* 65 *Psi:* 160
Service:	Cotton Spinning. 32 Rope drive

Urmsons were best known for their mill gearing, but did build about half a dozen large engines which were virtually a standard design, except for that at Hartford Mill (see SER 837). The high engine centre line, the brass catch box Corliss trip motion, the name plate attached by clips to the engine rails, and the twin slide tail rod supports were their usual features. The other mill, No2, was started as an electrically driven unit although it cost more, since there was no room for an additional cooling water lodge. Belgrave was a successful concern which was running independently into the late 1960s when so many had closed.

43. Oldham, The Coldhurst Spinning Co.   SER 497

Type:	Horizontal four cylinder triple expansion.
Photo taken:	1952
Maker and Date:	Buckley & Taylor, Oldham, 1898
Cylinder/dimensions:	22$^1/_2$ in, 35, 40in and 40in.
Hp: 1,250	*Rpm:* 40 *Psi:* 165
Service:	Cotton spinning. Coarse count. Geared drive.

This was the standard Buckley and Taylor design as used for rope and geared drive engines, but was unusual in that the intermediate pressure cylinder was fitted with a piston valve. Buckley and Taylor usually fitted Corliss valves as on the high pressure, or slide valves, as on the low pressure two here, only making a few piston valves. The drive was by teeth off the flywheel rim to a pinion on the second motion shaft and then by bevel wheels to the vertical shaft and floors. New main drive bevel wheels were purchased (cost £800), but were not fitted, as the mill went over to electric drive in 1952.

Publisher's note: George Watkins also added in manuscript: "The mill was [origi-nally] built in 1876, probably the engine was a twin tandem slide valve as [at] Commer-cial [Mill], and would be the earliest known example."

44. Oldham, James Greaves & Co, Derker Mills   SER 966

Type:	Horizontal twin tandem condensing
Photo taken:	1959
Maker and Date:	Buckley & Taylor, Oldham, 1897
Cylinder/dimensions:	17$^3/_8$ in and 38$^1/_4$ in x 4ft 6in each side-Piston valves
Hp: 1,000	*Rpm:* 61 *Psi:* 130
Service:	Weaving shed drive

This was Buckley and Taylor's design of the 1880s, before they were using Corliss valves. The piston valves were unusual for Buckley and Taylor, but certainly did very well here, as this and a Scott and Hodgson engine were steamed by three boilers only. The only known major work on the engine was a cylinder bed replaced by S.S.Stott. The plant was very well maintained and extremely quiet, but all of it was scrapped, including some 2,000 looms, when the business closed in the late 1950s. Greaves were unusual for Oldham, in that they were almost entirely cotton weavers whereas the town was the greatest of all cotton spinning areas in the world around 1900.

45. Oldham, Hague and Co., Hawthorn Mill   SER 717

Type:	Horizontal four cylinder triple expansion
Photo taken:	1955
Maker and Date:	George Saxon Ltd., Manchester, 1878
Cylinder/dimensions:	21in, 32in, 36in and 36in x 5ft 0in – Corliss and slide valves
Hp: 1,300	*Rpm:* 54 *Psi:* 180
Service:	Cotton spinning. Built with belt drive. Changed to ropes.

This was built by Saxon as a twin tandem compound with slide valve cylinders: they were 18in and 36in x 5ft 0in each side, developing 800 hp at 50 rpm, and driving by three 30in belts from a 28ft 0in flywheel, with steam at 90 psi. It was altered as noted above in 1909, and ran the very successful mill until it was decided to close it, demoli-tion following in 1970-71.

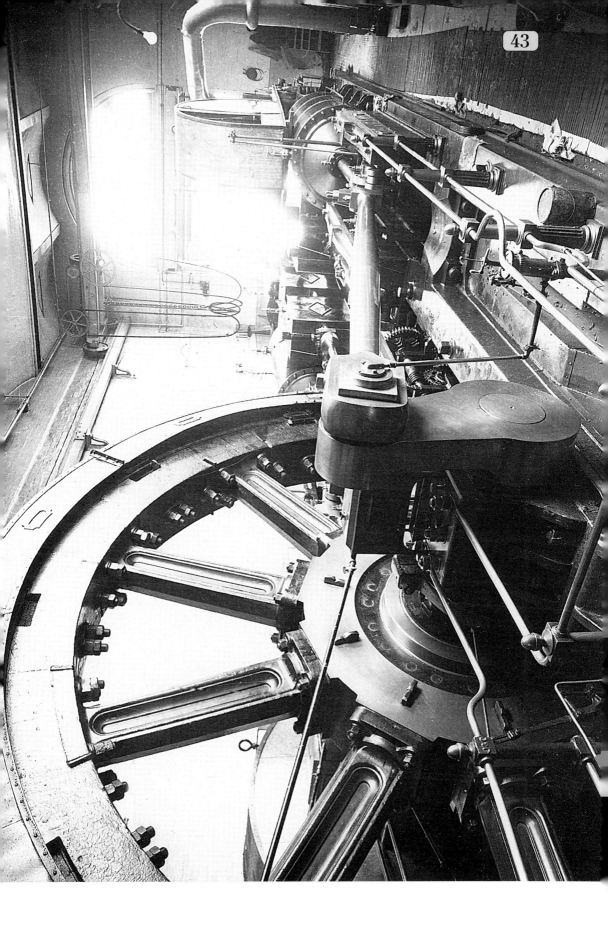

46. Oldham, John Hall & Co., Greengate Street   SER 364a

Type:	Pusher assisted beam.
Photo taken:	1951
Maker and Date:	Howard & Co., Rochdale. 1863
Cylinder/dimensions:	25in x 5ft 0in – Slide valves
Hp: 60	*Rpm:* 25 *Psi:* 25
Service:	Bobbin makers. Works drive by gears and ropes

The beam engine alone drove the works for 27 years using steam at about 20 psi, and even in the late 1950s was unaltered and indeed had little repair. It was a typical Lancashire engine, heavily made, but possibly the flywheel may have been replaced, as the arms of circular cross section seemed later. The drive was from the flywheel rim 15 feet diameter, to a pinion 7 feet diameter on the main shaft, below the engine room floor. There was probably another shaft driving to the right, driven by a pinion near to the top of the flywheel, otherwise the engine room scene was typical of the mid-19th century: plain and practical.

47. Oldham, John Hall & Co., Greengate Street   SER 364b

Type:	Horizontal single cylinder non-condensing
Photo taken:	1951
Maker and Date:	Maker unknown, c. 1890
Cylinder/dimensions:	15in x 5ft 0in
Hp: 60	*Rpm:* 25 *Psi:* 120
Service:	Bobbin makers. Assisted beam engine

The horizontal was as plain as the beam engine, and had equally little attention. It may have been installed to drive an addition to the works, as it was set away from the engine room wall, suggesting that the rope driving pulley was added when the crankshaft was replaced by a longer one for the horizontal engine to couple in. The jaw end for the connecting rod bearings at the crosshead was an old feature, but both engines were as simple as possible, the only additions being metallic piston rod packings and mechanical cylinder lubrication. The whole was scrapped when electrical driving was installed in 1945. The works closed in the mid-1950s, with the decline of the cotton trade.

48. Oldham, Iris Mill, Hathershaw   SER 363b

Type:	Gear drive wheel.
Photo taken:	1951
Maker and Date:	
Cylinder/dimensions:	
Hp:	*Rpm:* *Psi:*
Service:	Gear drive

This was by teeth upon the massive 21ft 0in diameter flywheel rim, to a pinion 6ft 6in diameter upon the mill second motion shaft. The curved casting seen carrying the handrail was a strut which maintained alignment between the two shafts, there being a strut at either side of the flywheel, the mill shaft being at the right.

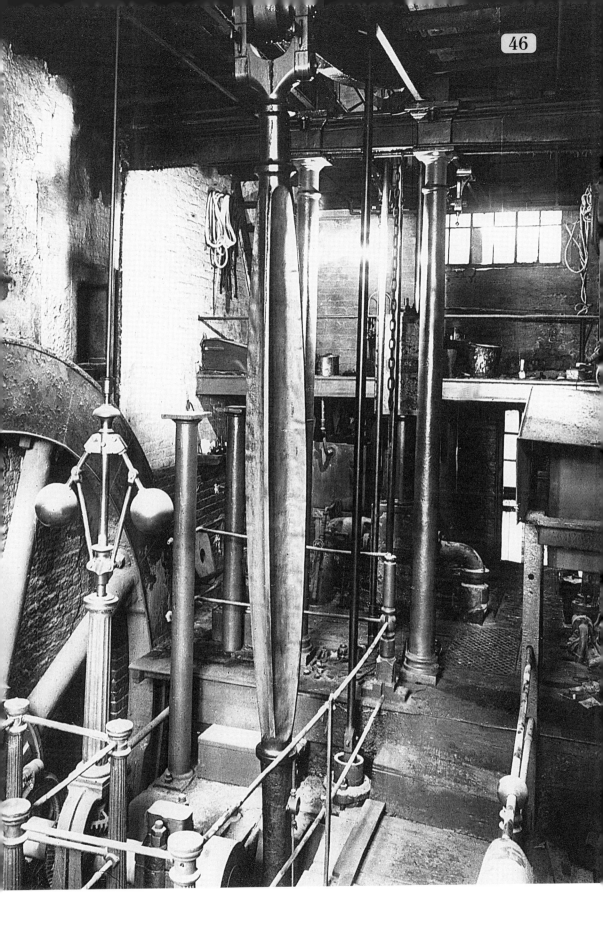

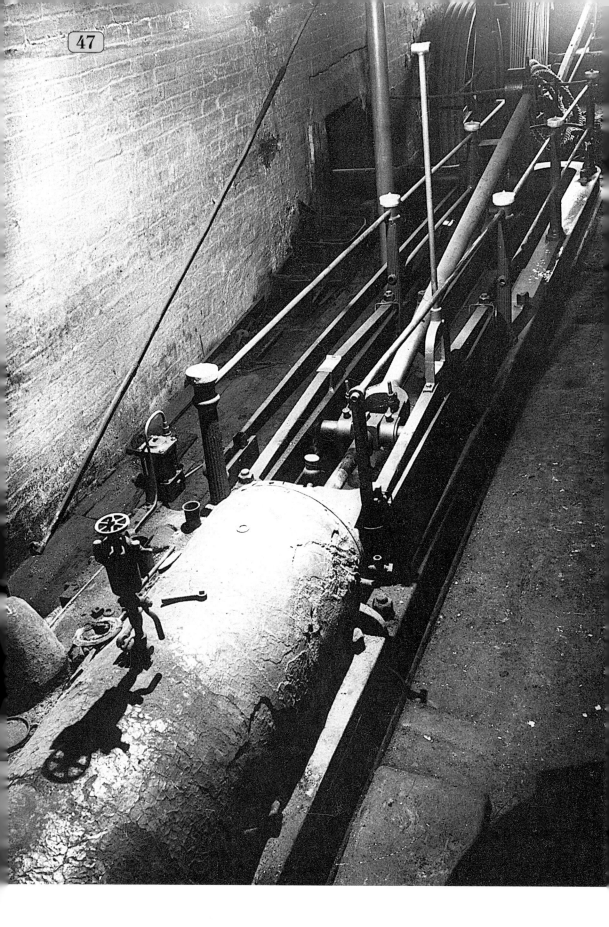

49. Oldham, Iris Mill, Hathershaw   SER 363c

Type:	High pressure cylinder.
Photo taken:	1951
Maker and Date:	Buckley & Taylor, 1898
Cylinder/dimensions:	34^1/$_2$ in x 3ft 0in-Corliss and piston valves.
Hp:	*Rpm:* *Psi:*
Service:	High pressure cylinder

The fitting of piston exhaust valves to cylinders with Corliss inlet was occasionally adopted by J. Tattersall in the 1890s, when he was a consultant engineer for mill repowering. The Tattersall & Baxter Corliss trip gear was also interesting, being fitted by him without licence payments when he designed the engine. The low pressure cylinders were the usual slide valve type.

50. Oldham, Eli Lees Mill   SER 1117

Type:	Weaving shed structure
Photo taken:	1963
Maker and Date:	No other data known.
Cylinder/dimensions:	
Hp:	*Rpm:* *Psi:*
Service:	Cotton spinning and weaving. Gear driven

There were two mills, on either side of the street, each originally with its own engine, and this was later changed to a single engine, to drive one mill by gearing and the other by ropes in a tunnel under the road. The engine was a cross compound horizontal by Buckley and Taylor, with gear drive off the flywheel arms, which, probably due to the following rope drive, was extremely noisy and regarded as such in an area where noisy heavy gearing was common. Although the engine house was unpleasantly hot as well as noisy, the plant ran the two mills (the one driven by ropes and vertical shaft was seven floors high) successfully and economically compared with the two engines, until closed (possibly in the late 1940s), when all was scrapped.

51. Oldham, Lees & Wrigley Ltd   SER 504

Type:	Double McNaught beam
Photo taken:	1952
Maker and Date:	Buckley & Taylor
Cylinder/dimensions:	29in x 3ft 9in-Corliss valves; 45in x 7ft 0in-slide valve
Hp: 1196	*Rpm:* 30 *Psi:* 160
Service:	Cotton spinning gear drive

This was similar to SER 502 and later was greatly overloaded, with a very massive flywheel to assist even turning. Despite this, it gave very good service, the mill running fully until closure in the 1950s. There were four engines, two beam and two horizontal and two boiler plants with over a dozen boilers, and there was also No. 5 mill which was built for electric driving in the 1930s, although possibly little if ever used. The size can be assessed from the man nearly 6ft. tall seen beside the high pressure cylinder. Everything was scrapped at the closure.

52. Oldham, Lees & Wrigley (No. 4 Mill)   SER 729b

Type: Horizontal compound pusher.
Photo taken: 1958
Maker and Date: Buckley & Taylor
Cylinder/dimensions: 16in and 35in x 3ft 6in – Corliss and slide valves
Hp: 1,300
Service: Assist no 729a

It was interesting that the last large mill beam engine should be fitted with a pusher assisting engine, a practice introduced by Fairbairn in the 1840s. It was needed at No.4 Mill since the machinery needed more than the estimated power, but this was not the only mill in which this occurred in the early 1900s.

53. Oldham, Park Bridge Ironworks   SER 722

Type: Inverted vertical cross compound condensing
Photo taken: 1955
Maker and Date: Buckley & Taylor, Oldham, 1909
Cylinder/dimensions: 15 in and 27in x 3 ft 0 in – slide valves.
Hp: 350   *Rpm:* 85   *Psi:* 90
Service: Works drive. Textile machine roller and spindle makers.

This drove the main spindle and roller making machinery by 10 ropes to the mainshaft and many belts to machinery. It was due to be replaced by electric motors in 1954, and the works were closed with trade recession in the 1960s.

54. Oldham, Abraham Stott & Co, Osborne Mill, Busk   SER 968b

Type: Parsons steam turbine
Photo taken: 1959
Maker and Date: Chas. Parsons and Co., Newcastle, 1921
Cylinder/dimensions:
Hp: 980   *Rpm:* 3000/350 ?   *Psi:*
Service: Cotton spinning. 30 rope drive.

This replaced both a beam engine and a Petrie's horizontal engine, and was said to be one of the earliest roped steam turbine drives, but this is doubtful. It was extremely compact and was not noisy, and had been a very good drive, as indeed was the engine shown at SER 968a. Certainly they were highly economical units, running on three oil fired boilers which were new in 1956. The mill was certainly running in the mid-1960s, but cotton spinning had declined by 1970 in Oldham.

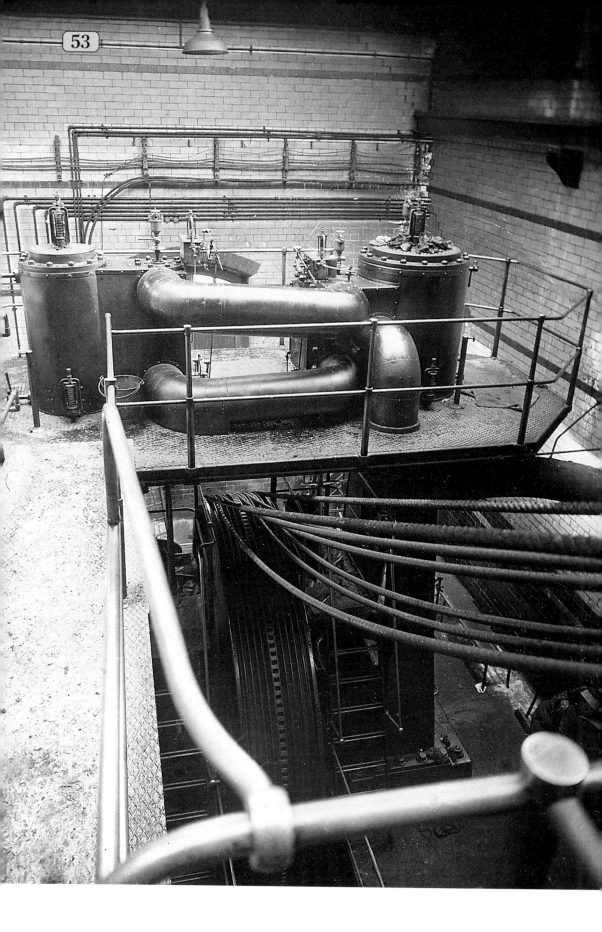

55. Oldham, Abraham Stott & Co, Osborne Mill, Busk   SER 968a

Type:	Horizontal cross compound condensing
Photo taken:	1959
Maker and Date:	Hick Hargreaves & Co., Bolton. About 1907
Cylinder/dimensions:	23in and 47in x 4ft 6in – Corliss valves
Hp: 1200	*Rpm:* 75 *Psi:* 160
Service:	Cotton spinning. Drive by 32 ropes off 21ft flywheel.

This was Hick's latest design with the high speed crab-claw Corliss trip gear and the lagging and oil splash guards were particularly neat. The triangular wrist plate and dash pots close to the trip gear and single tail rod slides, and the flywheel arm lagging close to the arms, and only splayed out at the rim, are all late Hick's design details. The mills were certainly running in the late 1960s with the steam drive. The engine room was very plain, although nothing was skimped in the general layout.

56. Oldham, The United Mill Co., Chadderton   SER 709

Type:	Horizontal twin tandem compound condensing
Photo taken:	1955
Maker and Date:	Pollit and Wigzell, 1876
Cylinder/dimensions:	20in and 39 in x 5ft 0in each side – Corliss and slide valves.
Hp: 1,800	*Rpm:* 72 *Psi:* 160
Service:	Cotton spinning. Geared drive.

United Mill was built with twin tandem Pollit engines with slide valves and boilers for 80-100 psi, and new boilers and cylinders for higher steam pressure and power were fitted in 1902. The engines ran faster than most geared drives and the whole was very noisy, since the whole of the gearing and the vertical shafts were also in the engine room. The mill drive to the five floors was split between two vertical shafts, driving three floors off one, and two off the other vertical shaft. The gearing was also supplied by Pollit and Wigzell, and remained unaltered.

57. Oldham, The United Mill Co., Chadderton   SER 709a

Type:	Spur and bevel wheels
Photo taken:	1955
Maker and Date:	Pollit and Wigzell
Cylinder/dimensions:	
Hp:	*Rpm:* *Psi:*
Service:	Geared main drives.

The main drive was by a ring of spur teeth upon the flywheel arms, as seen at the left, this being smaller than the massive flywheel rim, which nearly touched the driven or second motion shaft i.e. the flywheel was 14ft 6in diameter, the spur toothed ring was 10ft diameter, driving to the pinion 5ft 6in diameter, inside the casing. The driven shaft was the full width of the engine room, with a bevel wheel at each end driving to two vertical shafts, one of which is seen at the right hand side. This drove the upper three floors, which were spinning cotton, and the bevels at the other end of the second motion shaft drove a similar vertical shaft which, however, drove only two floors driving the preparation machinery which was always the heaviest load in cotton spinning.

58. Oldham, Whittaker and Co.   SER 538

Type:	Engineers' shop
Service:	General engineers and wheelwrights.

In the centre of the photograph is the high pressure cylinder from Fitton's Shawside mill beam engine (see SER 502) which was fractured in service and at Whittakers for replacement. Frank Wightman is seen, with calipers, beside it as he was measuring it for drawings for the patternmakers to make the replacement. It was a complex casting comprising the stool and valve chest in one with the cylinder barrel, and measuring was difficult. The box slide valve is seen near the stool and beside the base of the cylinder on the stool is the flat plate cut-off valve fitted by Scott & Hodgson early in the 1900s. Behind is seen a Corliss valve cylinder for an unknown mill, and on the stools at the left hand side is a Wheelock valve box for a horizontal rolling mill engine in the Midlands. The lad at the side was an apprentice, and the whole is typical of the engineers' shops of Lancashire.

59. Openshaw, Manchester, Hampson, Wrigley & Co.   SER 895

Type:	Horizontal single tandem	
Photo taken:	1958	
Maker and Date:	J Robinson, Openshaw, Manchester, 1907.	
Cylinder/dimensions:	15in and 30in x 3ft 0in – Corliss valves	
Hp: 500	*Rpm:* 84	*Psi:* 140
Service:	Textile finishing works drive. 12 ropes.	

This was very near to the site of Robinson's works, which appear to have closed in 1930, and replaced a large beam engine with gear drives. The general design resembled that of S. S. Stott, of Haslingden, being massive, with a single slipper crosshead guide and rounded crank webs. It had very little alteration in its lifetime, or little repair, and probably ran the works until they were closed in the 1960s. The general finish of the engine was good, but the fluff and dirt of textile finishing on the lubricating grease made it difficult to keep clean. The Corliss valve gear was Robinson's own patent type.

60. Oswaldtwistle, Shaw & Co, Rhyddings Mill   SER 785

Type:	Double beam, altered	
Photo taken:	1956	
Maker and Date:	W. & J. Yates, Blackburn, c.1856.	
Cylinder/dimensions:	22in and 36in x 6ft 0in – Slide valves	
Hp: 247	*Rpm:* 31	*Psi:* 85
Service:	Cotton weaving. Gear drive off flywheel rim.	

The mill was projected as a combined spinning and weaving unit (frequent about the 1850s) but the spinning part was never completed, again a feature of the period when it was often found cheaper to buy than to spin yarn. It was built as a double McNaught type but with the final decision to abandon spinning, this was far larger than necessary for weaving alone. It was altered to cross compound in 1895 by Clayton, Goodfellow and ran very economically until about 1960, when it was decided to change production over to the newer shed with all electric drive, when the old works and the engine were scrapped. The boiler for the engine was said to have been of wrought iron, so may have been older than the new cylinders.

61. Padiham, G Green & Co., Green Lane Shed   SER 1159

Type:	Horizontal cross compound
Photo taken:	1964
Maker and Date:	Burnley Ironworks Co., 1909
Cylinder/dimensions:	12in and 24in x 3ft 0in – Corliss valves.
Hp: 200	*Rpm:* 86 *Psi:* 160
Service:	Cotton weaving. 8 rope drive of 12ft flywheel.

This was one of two removed from Burnley Electricity Works in 1911, when turbines were installed. It replaced a McNaughted beam engine and gear drives, and was placed in a new engine room in front of the old one. An additional shed was added at the same time, and needed all of the power the new engine could develop. Called *Isabella* and *Evelyn*, it certainly was a very good servant, and a great credit to the "Old Shop" that built it, as beside heavy loading at the generating station, it ran an evening shift at the shed for many years, running 15 hours daily. The plant was changed to automatic motor-driven looms in the mid 1960s, and the engine had been scrapped by 1968.

62. Padiham, Padiham Waste Co.   SER 1187

Type:	Horizontal compound. Pickup's patent, 1880s ?
Photo taken:	1965
Maker and Date:	Wm Bracewell & Co., Burnley, 1870s
Cylinder/dimensions:	HP 18in x 2ft 0in, LP 24in x 3ft 0in – Slide valves.
Hp: 200	*Rpm:* 80 *Psi:* 100
Service:	Cotton weaving. 24in belt drive to shed.

Pickup's patent consisted of making the high and the low pressure cylinders of different strokes, the high pressure being shorter to allow the air pump to be placed between the cylinder and the crank. This can be seen at the right hand cylinder in the print, with the low pressure driving directly to the crank at the left. The engine had driven to the shed by a wide belt to the mainshaft. Weaving had so long ceased at the plant, however, that when after a fire at the waste warehouse had revealed the engine's existence (no-one knew it had survived as that part was not used by the occupiers, dealing in cotton waste) no record of the owners could be found. It was certainly the last surviving example of the design which was made in vertical as well as horizontal forms. It was too damaged to be saved , although it was rare.

63. Pemberton, Enfield Manufacturing Co.   SER 862

Type:	Horizontal single tandem condensing
Photo taken:	1957
Maker and Date:	T. T. Crook, Stanley Ironworks, Bolton, 1908
Cylinder/dimensions:	13in and 23in x 3ft 0in – Corliss and slide valves.
Hp: 250	*Rpm:* 80 *Psi:* 145

Thos. Crook was a small foundry and engineering shop which made a wide range of machinery for the brickmaking trade, i.e. brick presses, pan mills also a large range of mortar mixing machines. They had their own foundry, and pattern-making shops, and this was almost the only large engine that they made. It was certainly very good, and well loaded, gave very little trouble, and was fitted with a Pickering throttle governor as well as Crook's governor which altered the cut-off of the Corliss valve gear. The shed side shaft was 120ft long and drove the looms by 12 bevel wheel driven cross shafts. A single boiler by Foster of Preston ran the engine until the mill was closed in the cotton re-organisation scheme in 1960. It was always well kept. (See SER No.1403 for Crook's works, Vol. 3.1 p.52).

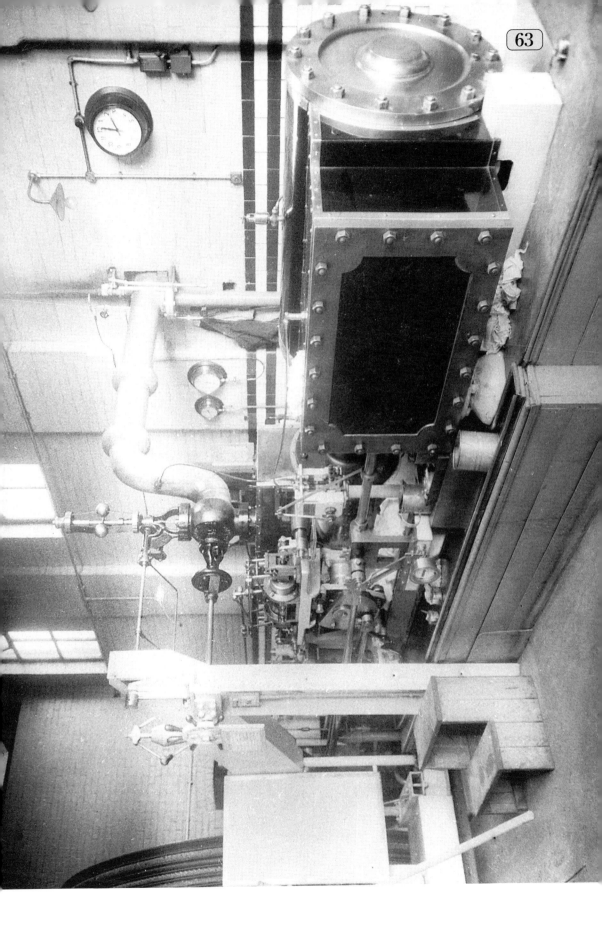

64. Prescot, St. Helens Waterworks, Eccleston Hill Pumping Station SER 801

Type:	Horizontal tandem compound condensing
Photo taken:	1956
Maker and Date:	Robert Daglish & Co., St. Helens, 1897
Cylinder/dimensions:	Approx. 18in and 32in x 3ft 6in – Slide valves
Hp: 120?	*Rpm:* 25 *Psi:* 100
Service:	Town supply from wells.

This replaced two Cornish beam engines in the same house, but nothing was known of them, and this engine, too, was superseded by electrically driven pumps in the 1950s. The well was at the rear of the engine with the pumps driven from bell cranks in the framing above the well, and with the single ram surface lift pump driven from the bell crank nearer to the engine. There were two pumps in the well with two bell cranks. The engine was plain but neat, and the whole station an attractive mid-Victorian complex. The steam plant was scrapped later but the wells are still used with the new pumps.

65. Preston, John Barnes & Sons, Waverley Park Shed   SER 906

Type:	Uniflow
Photo taken:	1958
Maker and Date:	John Musgrave & Sons Ltd., Bolton, 1914
Cylinder/dimensions:	$26^1/_2$ in x 3ft 0in
Hp: 400	*Rpm:* 130 *Psi:* 160
Service:	Cotton weaving. Direct drive to the mainshaft.

This appears to have been originally built with the side shaft drive for the valves, possibly as a result of the troubles caused by the differing expansions of the cylinder and the layshaft noted in SER 905. Certainly there were pads cast on the frame and cylinder originally for the brackets carrying the rotating high level camshaft operating the valves, the camshaft being driven by chains and bevel gears from the crankshaft. There was the usual vertical governor off the crankshaft, controlling the cut-off by sliding rollers between the cams and the valve operating rocking levers, giving lighter loading on the governor. The engine was in regular use until the mill was closed about 1960. It was the only instance of this design of valve gear that I met, and certainly overcame the expansion trouble, which actually caused a difference in the cut-off in the front and back of the cylinder.

66. Preston, Emerson Road Mill   SER 1185

Type:	Horizontal cross compound.
Photo taken:	1965
Maker and Date:	Ashton, Frost & Co., Blackburn, 1907
Cylinder/dimensions:	12in and $23^1/_2$ in x 2ft 6in – Corliss and slide valves
Hp: 250	*Rpm:* 98 *Psi:* 130
Service:	Cotton weaving. 8 rope drive off 19ft 6in flywheel.

The plant was typical of the last great expansion period of the English cotton trade, and the engine gave little trouble in nearly sixty years work. Called *Seacome* (L.P. side) it was a typical Ashton's shed engine, with the boiler feed pump driven from the low pressure slide valve tail rod, taking the feed water directly from the condenser beside it. It ran with saturated steam until 1939, when Bolton's superheaters were fitted, and these were replaced by Swansea Unit type superheaters some twelve years later. A new economiser was also installed in 1961. The little plant was regrettably compelled to close from poor trade in 1965; all was sold and the engine scrapped.

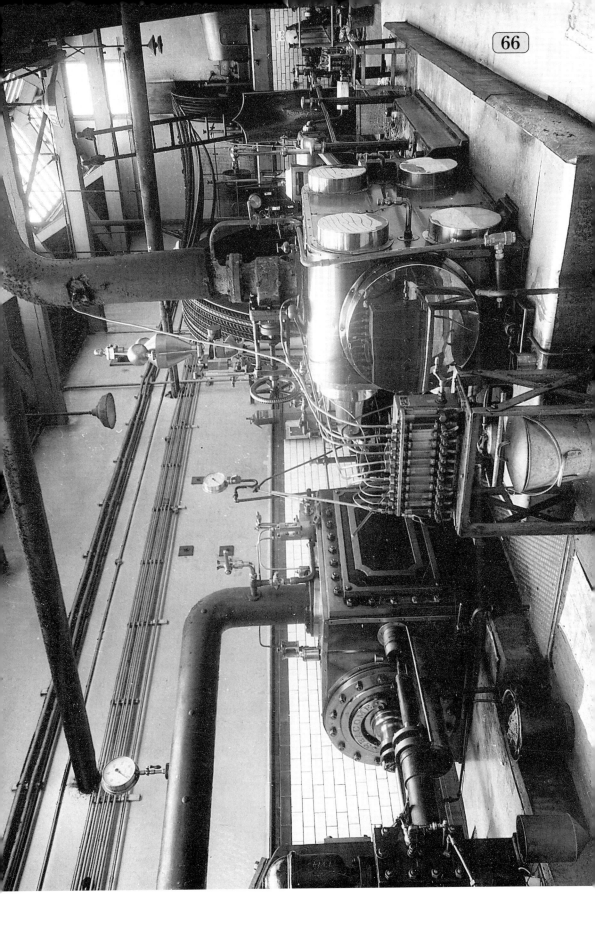

67. Preston, Horrockses, Crewdson Ltd., Fishwick Mill   SER 1031

Type:	Inverted vertical cross compound
Photo taken:	1960
Maker and Date:	Yates & Thom, Blackburn, 1892
Cylinder/dimensions:	Approx. 24in and 48in x 5ft 0in – Corliss valves
Hp: 1,100	*Rpm:* 64 *Psi:* 160
Service:	Cotton weaving. 26 rope drive to shed mainshaft, alternator, and winding room.

Named *The William* and *The Edmund*, this was largely unaltered in some 65 years of heavy work on the weaving side of the very large Horrockses' business. It was a large engine for a weaving shed, and was over 30ft high. The open flywheel arms were unusual as they lost some power. There were 31 cross shafts to drive the looms which probably exceeded 2,000 at times, and all would be at work, when all of the power would be needed. It is probable that the high pressure cylinder had been renewed, but the low pressure was original and still retained the mahogany lagging of 1892. There was general changeover to electrical drives from the grid in the 1950s, but the mills did not survive very long afterwards. The steam engines (four or five) were scrapped. The use of parallel motion to guide the air pump bucket rod was an unusual feature of this engine.

68. Radcliffe, Walker Allen & Co.   SER 1415

Type:	Horizontal double cylinder
Photo taken:	1970
Maker and Date:	W.H. Bailey & Co ., Manchester, c. 1890s
Cylinder/dimensions:	10in x 1ft 3in – Slide valves
Hp: ?	*Rpm:* 100 *Psi:* 80
Service:	Fire and general water supply. Textile finishers.

The works had closed and all was being dismantled in 1970, this being almost the last intact unit. It was a standard Bailey design, of massive proportions and very plain, with two opposed plunger pumps at the rear of each cylinder, driven by a piston tail rod. It was about 12ft 6in overall length, with all of the engine solidly coupled together lengthwise, and mounted upon a plain concrete bed. Mainly for fire service these were always kept in steam, for instant operation when they were connected to a sprinkler system, when reduced water pressure would start the pump working. They were thus very valuable and saved a great deal in insurance costs, and were well kept and regularly tested. This one may well have provided water for the mill services as well. The main driving engine of the works had been a delightful small tandem by Walmsley, but this had long disappeared. Fire pumps of all types were a usual feature of textile plants where the fire risk was very great.

69. Radcliffe, The East Lancashire Paper Mill Co.   SER 1230

Type:	Horizontal tandem extraction.
Photo taken:	1966
Maker and Date:	John Musgrave & Sons Ltd., Bolton, 1926
Cylinder/dimensions:	37in and 53in x 3ft 8in
Hp: 2,500	*Rpm:* 112 *Psi:* 160
Service:	Pulping beater shaft and generator drive. Low pressure steam pass out.

This was one of the two largest engines that Musgraves built, and these two were almost at the end of their engine building. The other went to Peterculter Paper Co. near Aberdeen. (SER 1264, see Vol 2). They were the peak of fine engine work, very well made, and highly economical, since they were planned to pass out up to 20,000lbs of steam at 12 psi per hour to the process heating system. They were also economical as power engines, as the low pressure cylinders were uniflow, and so able to develop power economically even when the supply to process was high, and little going to the low pressure cylinder. The flywheel was very heavy – 16ft diameter, 2ft 6in wide and 1ft 6in deep, the drive to generator and the pulping mill being both direct from the crankshaft. Turbines and electrical driving had largely been adopted at Peterculter and Radcliffe over the years, and the engines were standby only by the late 1960s.

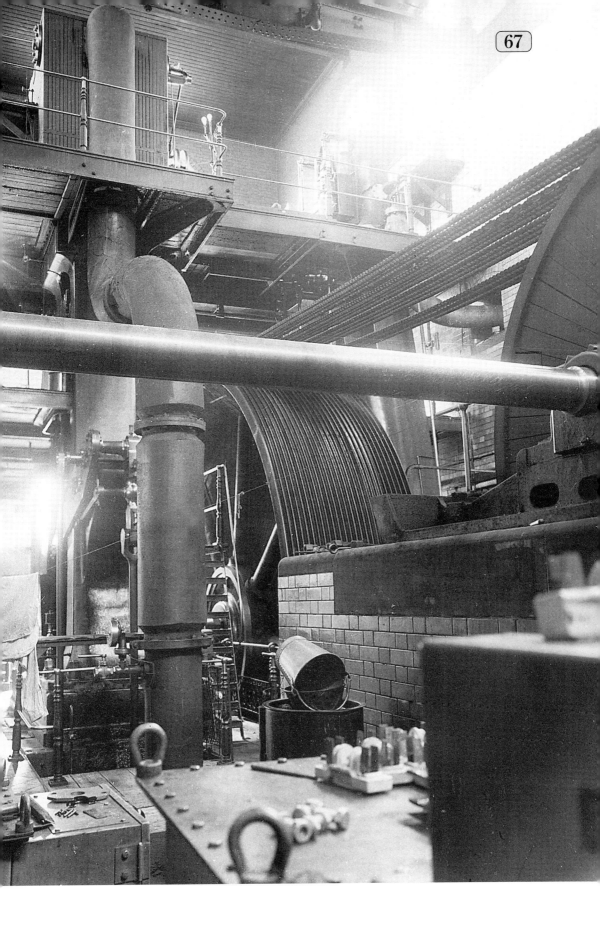

70. Radcliffe, Hardcastle & Co.   SER 1156a

Type:	Horizontal single tandem
Photo taken:	1964
Maker and Date:	Lancaster & Tonge, early 1900s
Cylinder/dimensions:	9in and 18in x 2ft 0in
Hp: 80	*Rpm:* 90 *Psi:* 80
Service:	Mill drive by 6 ropes off 5 ft pulley. Textile finishers.

Lancaster & Tonge were best known for their steam specialities, such as metallic packings, steam separators etc, and particularly for re-boring cylinders rapidly at weekends. A large number of colliery winders were re-bored and fitted with new pistons and rings in a weekend, the cylinders having been gauged, and all prepared beforehand, often resulting in great economy where exhaust was to atmosphere. Hardcastle's engine was one of only three that Lancaster & Tonge made, but it was a very good one, which ran for nearly seventy years. After this electrical drives were installed throughout the works, to replace this and an Ashworth & Parker triple expansion engine rope driving another part of the plant, as well as the diagonal engines on the printing machines.

71. Radcliffe, Hardcastle & Co.   SER 1156b

Type:	Five double diagonal
Photo taken:	1964
Maker and Date:	Various makers, early 1900s
Cylinder/dimensions:	6in, $7^1/_2$ in bore x 8in, 9in-slide valves
Hp:	*Rpm:* *Psi:*
Service:	Textile printing machine drives.

The colour printing machines needed very close speed control, and also needed low pressure steam for the drying drums over which printed cloth passed. This can be seen in the machine at the right hand side of the photograph. It was therefore convenient to fit separate engines to each machine, as the exhaust was fully used in drying, and each machine kept under full control. The exhaust steam was delivered to the heating main, not to the drum on the machine, at about 5-6 psi. Such engines were very popular in the finishing trades, sometimes over a dozen working in one shop. They were wasteful as power units, however, and later electrical drives were adopted, but they were very costly for variable speeds.

72. Radcliffe, A & J Hoyle Ltd., Park Street Shed   SER 1157

Type:	Non dead centre compound.
Photo taken:	1964
Maker and Date:	John Musgrave & Sons Ltd., Bolton, 1934
Cylinder/dimensions:	$10^1/_2$ in and $16^1/_2$ in x 1ft 9in-Rocking slide valves.
Hp: 100	*Rpm:* 110 *Psi:* 90
Service:	Weaving shed drive. 5 ropes to shed off 4ft pulley and 4 ropes off 8ft 6in flywheel to dynamo.

This was the smallest mill engine of this type that Musgraves made, although they did make smaller examples for electrical generating etc., such as that in the Science Museum. The mill was one of the earliest in the area to adopt electric lighting, and the engine drove the Royce 100 volt generator until the changeover to Grid current. The engine was in sound condition at the end of 70 years work, often overloaded with the lighting, as well as the shed load, but little but routine repairs were ever needed. The engine was kindly donated to the Northern Mill Engine Society after the changeover to electrical drive.

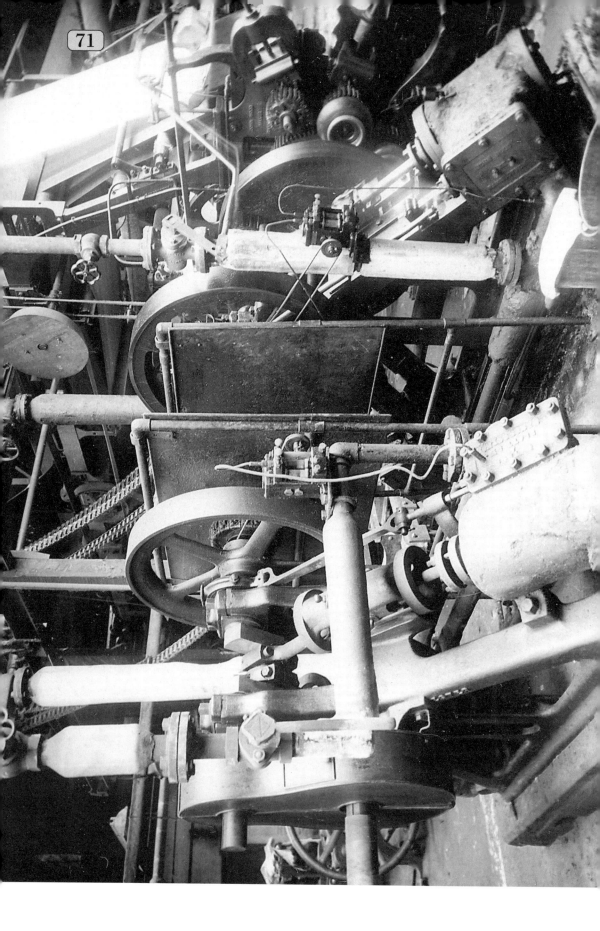

73. Radclife, John B. Lomax & Co.   SER 1414

Type:	Two double diagonal
Photo taken:	1970
Maker and Date:	Unknown
Cylinder/dimensions:	6 in x 9in – slide valves.
Hp: 7-8	*Rpm:* 100 *Psi:* 80
Service:	Drying and printing machine drives. Direct coupled. Textile finishers.

These were standard driving engines for the textile finishers' printing and drying machines, in which the finished cloth was passed over numerous steam heated rollers heated by low pressure, and the exhaust steam from the engines. Sturdy and simple, they needed to be, as the machine hands grossly abused the little work horses, which were frequently not even oiled during the periods they were stopped. Wear was thus heavy as, too, was the duty at times, yet with infinitely variable speed and great overload capacity, they worked for many years (well over half a century was common). In a works with up to a dozen of them, one, two or possibly three would be allocated to each fitter for maintenance. Few, however, remained by 1970, as the finishing trade died off, and these were part of possibly a dozen which remained out of hundreds once used.

74. Radcliffe, Mount Sion Bleachworks   SER 1417

Type:	Middle breast water wheel and beam pump.
Photo taken:	1970
Maker and Date:	Unknown, early 19th century
Cylinder/dimensions:	12ft diameter x 5ft wide
Hp:	*Rpm:* 10-12 *Psi:*
Service:	Works water supply by two ram pumps. 14in diameter x 3ft stroke.

This is a very early type of plant supplying the bleachworks lodge, some 20ft above, with water from the River Irwell, and driven by a fall in the Irwell at that point. The fall is about 8ft, and the river flow would have provided power to several wheels in other works along the river there. The entire water power capacity of the Irwell was utilised before 1810, and was the basis for the intense industrial development along the river, which was then literally lined with textile plants. Bleaching required large amounts of water for washing out the chemicals used to clear the cloth to whiteness. The beams were about 10ft long, and were 12ft above the waterwheel and drove the pumps directly by parallel motion. The ashlar stone structure carrying the beams was unusually massive even for so early. The date was unknown, but the Lever Bank bleachworks, the next down the river, was started in 1804.

75. Ramsbottom, J. Ashworth & Co., Wood Road Mill, Summerseat SER 1057

Type:	Horizontal cross compound
Photo taken:	1961
Maker and Date:	J. Petrie & Co., Rochdale? Date unknown.
Cylinder/dimensions:	16in and 28in x 4ft 0in – Slide valve
Hp: 250	*Rpm:* 60 *Psi:* 100
Service:	Made cotton and woollen blankets. Gear drive.

The mill was old, possibly early 19th century, driven by a water wheel at first. A stone in the chimney was cut with "R.H & S, 1842" but nothing was known about this.

There was possibly also a beam engine at one time, again uncertain. The horizontal engine was certainly very old, possibly made by Petrie in the 1850-60s and was probably a twin cylinder simple expansion originally. Probably altered to cross compound in the 1890s, said to be the date of the Petrie boiler in use in 1959. The gear drive was by teeth on the flywheel rim 15ft diameter to an iron pinion 6ft diameter on the second motion shaft which was on the top of the engine framing to drive off to the left. The mill was interesting as it was built into the hillside, with weaving on two lower floors. It was probably closed in the early 1960s and all scrapped. It was a useful little plant which made up a discarded grade of material into a sound product.

76. Ramsbottom, Pemberton & Co., Peel Bridge Mills   SER 911

Type:	Horizontal cross compound
Photo taken:	1958
Maker and Date:	Ashton, Frost & Co., Blackburn, 1915
Cylinder/dimensions:	14in and 28in x 3ft 6in – Corliss and slide valves
Hp: 375	*Rpm:* 85 *Psi:* 160
Service:	Cotton weaving. Rope drive to shed mainshaft.

This was nearly the last shed engine Ashton, Frost built, possibly only followed by the one for Allenby Shed (1921?) which was similar in design. It was certainly well loaded at one time when there were 1,000 looms in the sheds (it was customary to allow one half horse power per loom in calculating the power of a shed engine, which allowed for the auxiliary loadings of hoists etc.,). In brisk trade it must have been taking steam for some 90% of the stroke, as most of the looms would be working. It is believed that the plant was scrapped when the mill was closed in the re-organisation scheme of 1960.

77. Rawtenstall, Clowes Mill, Bury Road   SER 103a

Type:	Single beam engine with horizontal pusher
Photo taken:	1935
Maker and Date:	J. Leese, Bury, 1838
Cylinder/dimensions:	24in x 4ft 6in – slide valve.
Hp:	*Rpm:* 40 *Psi:* 75
Service:	Cotton cloth weaving. Shed driven by spur drive to second motion with bevel drives to the loom shafts. Beam 15ft long. Flywheel 15ft diameter.

This was unaltered generally, but was rebuilt when the pusher engine was installed to drive the extra shed. A new, longer crankshaft was fitted to take the pusher engine crank, and a new short valve chest was fitted, since the pressure was higher (although it was the exhaust from the pusher) after the alterations. The taping shed was originally driven by a vertical shaft and bevel wheels, but was later converted to ropes.

78. Rawtenstall, Clowes Mill, Bury Road   SER 103b

Type:	Single horizontal pusher engine.
Photo taken:	1935
Maker and Date:	J. Furnevall, Haslingden. Date unknown.
Cylinder/dimensions:	15¼ in x 4ft 6in – slide valve.
Hp:	*Rpm:* *Psi:*
Service:	Assisted beam engine.

This was added in the 1870s when the second shed was constructed, built on the other side of the mill yard, driven by a cross shaft from the second motion. An interesting feature was that the cylinder of the horizontal engine was of a very old type with a long "D" type of valve, far more in keeping with the beam engine in fact, but the high speed governor was fitted after 1900.

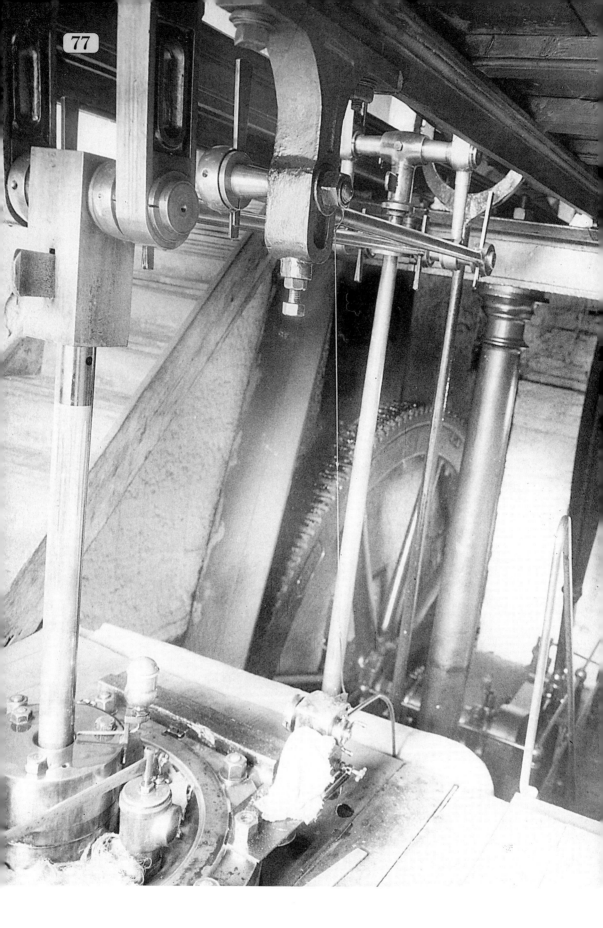

79. Rawtenstall, Hardman Bros., New Hall Hey Mill   SER 156

Type:	Pusher compound single beam.
Photo taken:	1935
Maker and Date:	S. S. Stott on beam engine valve chest? Date uncertain.
Cylinder/dimensions:	
Hp: *Rpm:* *Psi:*	
Service:	Geared drive, together with three water wheels. Horizontal added by Rothwell, Bolton, 1868. (Corliss cylinder fitted by Stott 1925). Closed 1950s?

This was very unusual in that the pusher HP engine was coupled to the beam engine by a drag link, and short secondary crankshaft. This was probably due to the gearing of the water wheels being the other side of the engine room wall, so preventing the horizontal from being coupled to the end of the shaft in the usual way. The whole worked very well with very little noise, and was efficient on fuel.

80. Reddish, Broadstone Mills Ltd   SER 643

Type:	Inverted vertical triple expansion
Photo taken:	1954
Maker and Date:	George Saxon Ltd., Manchester, 1906 & 1908
Cylinder/dimensions:	22in, 35in, 56in x 4ft 0in – Corliss valves
Hp: Approx 1,500   *Rpm:* 78$\frac{1}{2}$ *Psi:* 160
Service:	Cotton spinning. Rope drives. Nos. 1 & 2 Mills

Broadstone was a large plant with 262,500 mule spinning spindles and needing all the engines' power at times. The two mills were completely separate, each having its own boiler plant and chimney, each driving from separate rope races between the two mill blocks. The mills were closed in 1958, and all of the plant was scrapped. The premises were later used by an electrical manufacturing concern.

81. Reddish, Thos. Houldsworth & Co, South Mill   SER 644

Type:	Inverted vertical compound condensing.
Photo taken:	
Maker and Date:	Scott & Hodgson, 1911
Cylinder/dimensions:	25in, 56in x 4ft 0in – Corliss valves
Hp: *Rpm:* *Psi:*	
Service:	Cotton spinning. Rope drives.

The North and South Mills were originally driven by a single large beam engine between them, with underground second motion to vertical shafts to the floors. The North Mill was fitted with an 800 hp engine and rope drive by J. & E. Wood in 1902, and the South Mill was similarly altered in 1911. The engines gave very good service until the mills were closed and all of the plant scrapped about 1958.

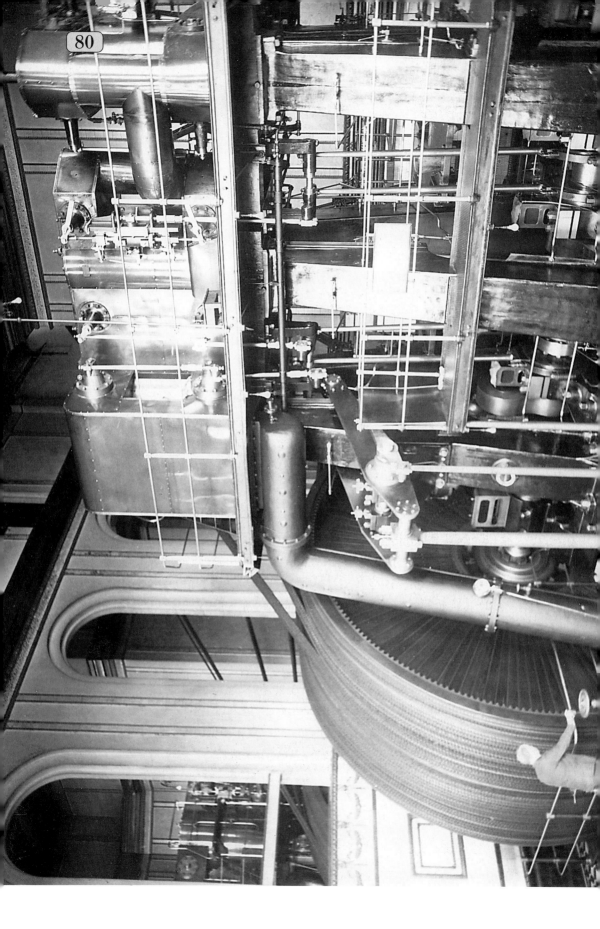

82. Reddish, Spur Doubling Co.　　　　　　　　　SER 645

Type:	Horizontal cross compounding condensing.
Photo taken:	
Maker and Date:	Scott & Hodgson, 1910
Cylinder/dimensions:	18in, 40in x 4ft 6in – Corliss valves.
Hp: 900	*Rpm:* 70　　　　　　*Psi:* 170
Service:	Double spinning of yarn to improve quality. 18 rope drive to single pulley.

This was probably a new plant in 1910, with a single mainshaft running at high speed. A typical Scott and Hodgson engine having the later type of valve gear, it ran very well, but the mill suffered from the varying trade conditions, and finally closed about 1960, all the plant being scrapped.

83. Rishton, Britannia Mill Co., Spring Street　　　　SER 907

Type:	Horizontal single tandem.
Photo taken:	1958
Maker and Date:	Ashton, Frost & Co., Blackburn, 1887
Cylinder/dimensions:	16in, 30in x 3ft 0in – slide valves
Hp: Approx 300	*Rpm:* 80　　　　　　*Psi:* 120
Service:	Cotton weaving. Rope drive. 490 looms in 1914

This was built as a tandem, the bed having faces for both cylinders machined upon it. A Clayton, Goodfellow drop cut-off valve was added later, but when a Lumb governor was fitted, the cut-off valve was removed, and the engine was run on throttle control. The condenser was tandem, behind the low pressure cylinder, with the boiler feed pump driven by the low pressure valve tail rod. It was the simplest type of engine that would economically drive a small weaving shed. The plant was closed in the reorganisation scheme of 1960.

84. Rishton, R. & T. Clayton, Bridgefield Mills　　　　SER 908

Type:	Horizontal single tandem.
Photo taken:	1958
Maker and Date:	Ashton, Frost & Co., Blackburn, 1884?
Cylinder/dimensions:	16in, 30in x 3ft 0in – Corliss and slide valves
Hp: Approx 220	*Rpm:* 60　　　　　　*Psi:* 120
Service:	Cotton weaving. No 2 shed. Gear drive.

This drove by double helical toothed gearing, which was very quiet, although the engine speed was higher than usual for gearing. The brackets for the various fittings suggested that it was built as in the photograph, with Corliss high pressure cylinder, and this may well be one of their earliest Corliss valve jobs. There were several variations from Ashton, Frost's design, and it could well have been a Clayton, Goodfellow originally, but both of R. & T. Clayton's engines suggested that Ashtons, and Clayton, Goodfellow worked on both of them indiscriminately; in fact this may originally have been a slide valve high pressure cylinder. Both engines had however, given very good service until the closure in 1960. There were two boilers which were on the canal side, and they must have been delivered, like the coal, by narrowboat.

85. Rochdale, Arkwright Mill   SER 899b

Type:	Horizontal twin tandem compound.
Photo taken:	1958
Maker and Date:	J Petrie & Co., Rochdale, 1885
Cylinder/dimensions:	Pistons, later Corliss valves.
Hp: 2,000	*Rpm:* 65 *Psi:* 160
Service:	Cotton spinning. 27 rope drive.

This was built with all piston valves to use steam at 80psi from Petrie's boilers and fitted with Petrie's twist cut-off motion. The load was always heavy, and at times exceeded 2,400 hp, using all four boilers. More power was required in 1914, and George Saxon then fitted the Corliss valve cylinders, and new boilers at the same time. A Lumb governor was also fitted later. The engine frames, crankshaft, flywheel and motion were unchanged, and it remained a Petrie's engine, despite the Saxon's name-plate fitted in 1914. The mill was closed about 1960. The average loading upon the ropes at this mill, i.e. 70hp each, was the highest that I met in Lancashire, but the original cylinders, 23in and 43in x 5ft would certainly have been designed for over 1,800 hp.

86. Rochdale, Crest Ring Mill   SER 594

Type:	Inverted vertical triple expansion
Photo taken:	1953
Maker and Date:	J Petrie & Co., Rochdale, 1907
Cylinder/dimensions:	21in, 34in, 56in x 4ft 0in – Corliss valves HP, piston valves on others.
Hp: 1,800	*Rpm:* 75 *Psi:* 190
Service:	Cotton spinning. Ring frames. Rope drive 32 ropes.

Petrie only made three engines of this type; the others went to the Marland Mill, Rochdale, and the Linnet at Gee Cross. The ring frames were a very heavy load, and required that the steam pressure be kept up to 190 psi, although the mill was only two floors. It was a high production plant, which used 120 tons of good coal per week at full load, using three of the four boilers. The half crank for the high pressure cylinder was unusual in a vertical engine, and here also a Lumb governor had been fitted later.

87. Rochdale, Dale Mill   SER 899a

Type:	Horizontal twin tandem compound
Photo taken:	1958
Maker and Date:	J. & W. McNaught, St George's Foundry, Rochdale, No. 1048, 1905
Cylinder/dimensions:	21in and 44in x 5ft 0in – Corliss and piston valves
Hp: 1,750	*Rpm:* 65 *Psi:* 160
Service:	Cotton spinning.

A typical McNaught's engine of the late period, this again has the low cross drive shaft for the high pressure valve gear. The rope drives were not very heavy for the power of the engine, i.e. about 30 hp per rope, whereas 50 hp was commonly accepted. This was an advantage however as lightly loaded drives lasted longer. The low pressure piston valves were originally fitted with twist cut off motion but this was disused in later years. A Lumb governor was fitted in the 1920s, but otherwise little was altered until the mill was closed about 1960. It was a very attractive engine room.

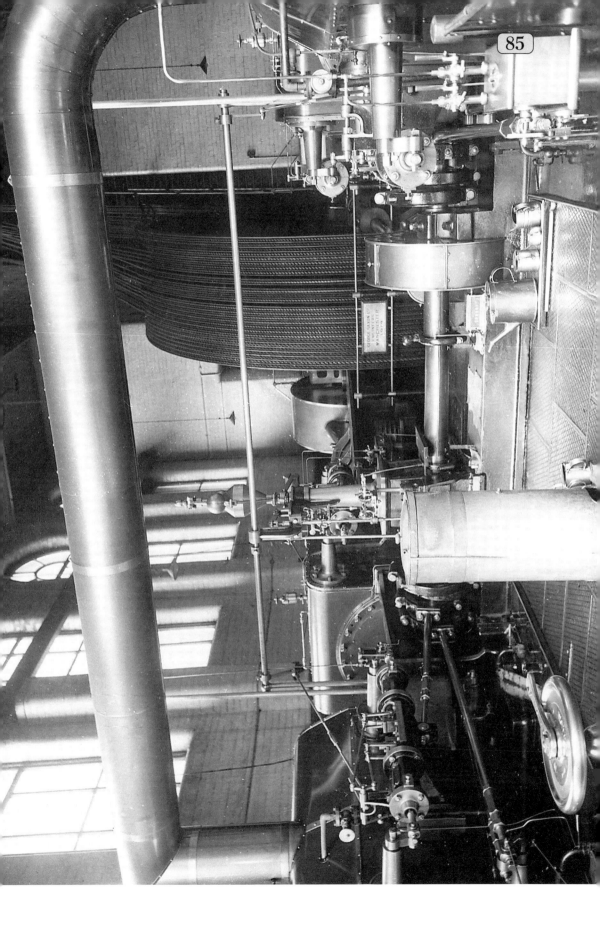

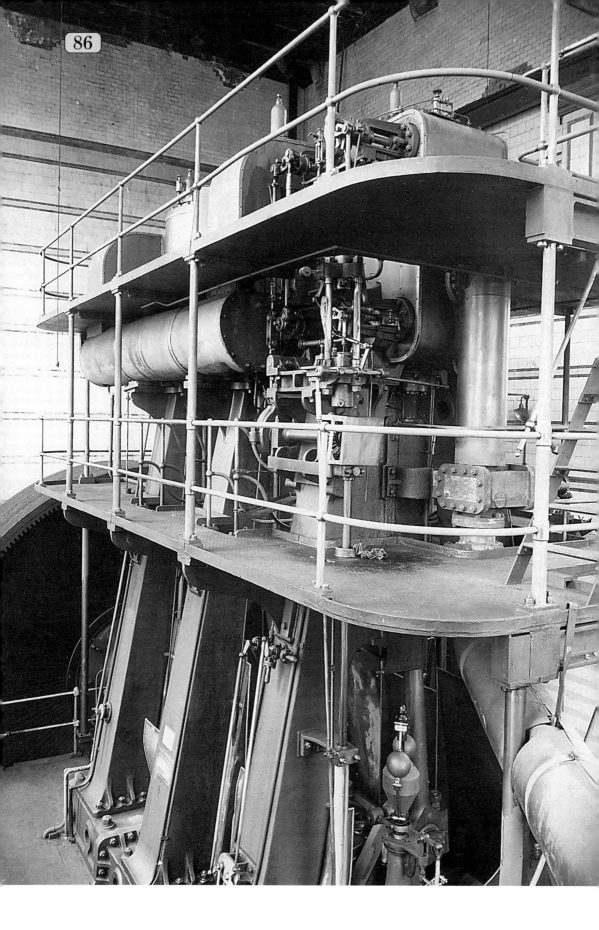

88. Rochdale, Ensor Mill Co., Castleton

SER 876a

Type:	Horizontal single tandem
Photo taken:	1957
Maker and Date:	Wm. Sharples & Co. Ramsbottom, 1908
Cylinder/dimensions:	$18^1/_2$in x 39 x 4ft 0in – Corliss valves.
Hp: 565	*Rpm:* $72^1/_2$ *Psi:* 165
Service:	Cotton spinning. 17 ropes off 22ft 0in flywheel.

This was one of Sharple's latest engines (they did not make many), but had Yates and Thom's Corliss trip motion fitted in place of the original Sharples gear, which resembled Musgrave's later type. A Lumb governor had been fitted later. Two engines were steamed by three oil-fired Lancashire boilers, and the mill was certainly well managed and successful. The low structure of the mills can be assessed from the fact that all of the ropes for No.1 worked in the single level rope race seen in the left hand side of the engine room. Compare this to SER 873.

89. Rochdale, Ensor Mill Co., Castleton, (No. 2 Mill)

SER 876b

Type:	Horizontal cross compound
Photo taken:	1957
Maker and Date:	Yates & Thom, 1915
Cylinder/dimensions:	19in and 40 in x 4ft 0 in – Corliss valves.
Hp: Approx. 600	*Rpm:* 73 *Psi:* 165
Service:	Cotton spinning. 21 rope drive off 22ft flywheel.

Ensor was unusual in that there were two mills separated by the engine room in which the two engines (one a tandem by Sharples of 1908) were placed back to back driving to the right and left. Another unusual feature was that the chimney was actually built on to the engine room wall originally, with a square base completed above the engine room by a circular top part. The engines continued to run into the 1970s – possibly the only ones in Rochdale to do so, and the mills were interesting in that there was only one driven floor with a small amount on another. The engine frame was trunk type.

90. Rochdale, Era Mill Co., Woodbine Street

SER 597

Type:	Horizontal four cylinder triple expansion
Photo taken:	1953
Maker and Date:	J. Petrie & Co., Rochdale, 1898
Cylinder/dimensions:	24in, 36in and two x 42in x 5ft 0in – Corliss and piston valves
Hp: 1,500 – 1,800	*Rpm:* 65 *Psi:* 160
Service:	Cotton spinning. Flywheel 26ft 0in diameter. 44 ropes.

Named *Victoria*, the main alterations to this in 60 years were the replacement of the high pressure cylinder about 1905, and the fitting of a Lumb governor, probably in the early 1900s. The four Petrie's boilers were still carrying the original steam pressure when fifty four years old. The mill was converted to electric drive in 1956 and the engine was scrapped.

91. Rochdale, S. & A. Heywood, Quarry Mill, Whitworth Road
SER 1103

Type:	Horizontal single cylinder condensing
Photo taken:	1962
Maker and Date:	J. Petrie & Co., Rochdale, c. 1890s
Cylinder/dimensions:	16in x 3ft 0in – Piston valves
Hp: 100	*Rpm:* 70 *Psi:* 70
Service:	Weaving shed. Direct shaft drive.

This was purchased secondhand from the Co-operative Society jam manufactory at Middleton, possibly when Heywoods took over the weaving shed about 1910. It ran well at the shed until the flywheel moved one afternoon, and rubbing the engine foundation caused a fire which damaged the engine too badly for repair. It was the last known small Petrie engine at work, and typical of their design in all ways. The condenser was at the rear of the engine under the floor. The piston valve was fitted with an internal twist type cut-off valve, under governor control, with Dowell's trip motion to allow quick closing under the dashpot, when the Dowell's trip released the valve. The main piston valve is recipro-cated by the eccentric, and the cut-off is by twisting the ported sleeves at the front and the rear in which the main valve moves. The plant continued to run with electrical drives.

92. Rochdale, Highams Ltd., Sudden
SER 938

Type:	Horizontal single tandem
Photo taken:	1958
Maker and Date:	J Petrie & Co., Rochdale, 1904
Cylinder/dimensions:	15$^1/_2$in and 29in x 4ft 0in – Corliss valves.
Hp: 350	*Rpm:* 85 *Psi:* 160
Service:	Textile finishing. Rope drive.

This was one of the 5 Petrie engines which were in the central power station of the Co-operative Society, Balloon St., Manchester, which were all removed when current was taken from public supply in 1914. This was said to have been a half of a twin tandem engine. It replaced a beam engine with a horizontal pusher engine in Highams's No. 1 mill, and was steamed by a Yates and Thom boiler of 1919. A new low pressure cylinder, also crank and con rod, was fitted by Saxon after a smash about 1937, and a new alternator was also fitted in 1957. The load was mainly electrical generating, and this was transferred to the grid in the mid-1960s, but the business closed soon after. The early Dowell's type trip gear was retained for the low pressure cylinder in the rebuild of 1937.

93. Rochdale, Moss Bridge Mill, Moss Bridge
SER 720

Type:	Horizontal cross compound
Photo taken:	1955
Maker and Date:	Woodhouse & Mitchell? Date unknown
Cylinder/dimensions:	16in and 30in x 3ft 0in – Corliss and slide valve
Hp: 350	*Rpm:* 85 *Psi:* 100
Service:	Cotton spinning. 10 rope drive.

The history of the engine was uncertain, but certainly Woodhouse & Mitchell had done work on it. The mill ran on until the mid-1950s, all being scrapped on closure. A secondhand Adamson boiler was fitted in 1939.

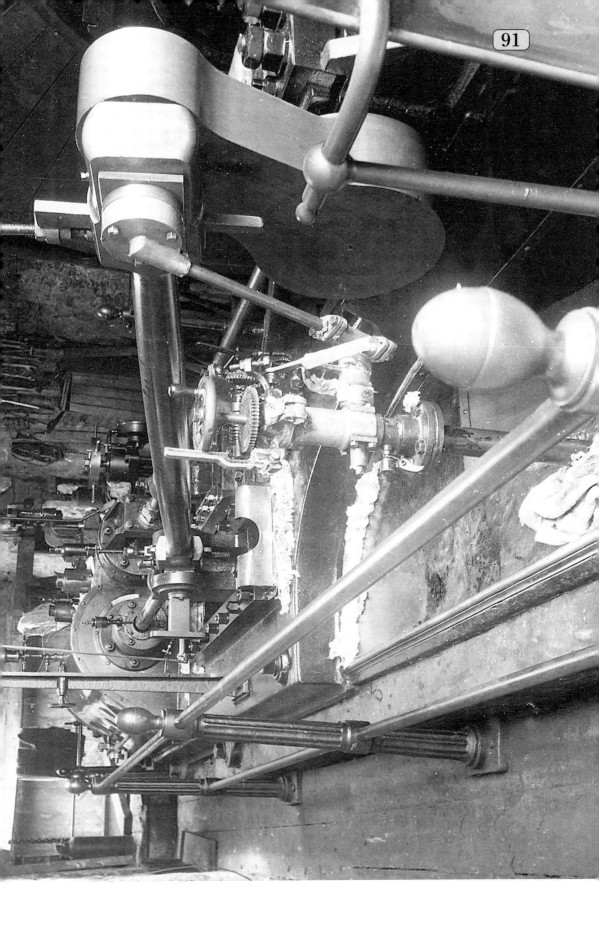

94. Rochdale, Moss Mill   SER 596

Type:	Horizontal twin tandem
Photo taken:	1953
Maker and Date:	J. Petrie & Co., Rochdale, 1890
Cylinder/dimensions:	24in and 45in x 6ft 0in each side – Corliss and piston valves
Hp: 2,000	*Rpm:* 60 *Psi:* 160
Service:	Cotton spinning. Rough waste cotton grades. Flywheel 30ft diameter. 44 ropes.

This was built with piston valves to all of the cylinders for 100 psi, and the Corliss valve high pressure cylinders together with four Petrie boilers for 160 psi were fitted probably in the early 1900s. The mill was converted to electric drive in 1958, and was still working in 1971. The typical Petrie struts between the cylinders are seen, and the governor was converted to the Lumb system.

   Publisher's note: In the SER record card system, which houses the 1,500 or so photos, this engine is SER 596. In the A3 size master list of engines held by the NMRC, it is recorded as 696.

95. Rochdale, T. Normanton & Co., Atlas Spring Works, Moss Street
SER 831

Type:	Unusual single tandem
Photo taken:	1956
Maker and Date:	Unknown, c. 1863?
Cylinder/dimensions:	16in and 30in x 3ft 0in – slide valves
Hp: Approx. 250	*Rpm:* 63 *Psi:* 70
Service:	Works drive. Geared.

The business was established by Messrs Leach in the 1860s, with a single cylinder engine, possibly by Barlow of Rochdale. The engine was rebuilt about 1893-4 (the date of the new boiler) and was probably altered at the same time, by placing a high pressure cylinder in between the crosshead guides and the crankshaft, so that there was a high pressure cylinder in front of the guides, with the connecting rod straddling it to drive to the crankshaft, and the low pressure in the original position at the rear. This probably meant that the new cylinders were of shorter stroke than the original single, but it gave higher power and economy with least alteration. The business passed to Normantons when the last of the Leach family, two old ladies, could not run it on. All the drives were converted to motors in the early 1960s.

96. Rochdale, Samuel O'Neill & Co, Castleton   SER 970

Type:	Horizontal single tandem.
Photo taken:	1959
Maker and Date:	J. Petrie & Co. Rochdale, 1909
Cylinder/dimensions:	19in and 34in x 3ft 6in – Drop valves
Hp: 450	*Rpm:* 84 *Psi:* 80
Service:	Tube and bobbin making for cotton trade.

There were two mill blocks on the site, of 1841 and 1894, and this was put in to replace the early beam with geared drives, and latterly drove the later mill as well. The drive was backwards to a second motion shaft which drove the heavy cross shaft in the foreground by gears from which rope drives were taken to the various floors of the mill. The engine was the Nuekomm type which Petries later adopted on engaging Mr. Nuekomm as designer, and like all his engines this gave very good service. The mill was damaged by fire in the late 1950s, but there was much electrical driving prior to the fire. The engine was broken up for scrap. The spur gears which connected the engine driven rope pulley and the cross shaft were in the room at the right which allowed good gear wheel sizes. It was quite quiet.

97. Rochdale, The Redcross Street Doubling Mill Co.   SER 593

Type:	Single tandem compound condensing
Photo taken:	1953
Maker and Date:	J. Petrie & Co., Rochdale, 1892
Cylinder/dimensions:	18in and 36in x 4ft 6in – Piston valves
Hp: 500	*Rpm:* 70 *Psi:* 100
Service:	Cotton doubling. 12 ropes.

This was a typical Petrie engine of the period, which was unaltered during its 70 years of running. The high pressure cylinder valve was fitted with the Dowell-type twist cut-off under control of the governor, and the stay at the top of the high and low pressure cylinders was a Petrie's design feature. The engine ran the opposite way to usual, and the ropes also drove back to behind the engine. It is reasonably certain that it replaced a beam engine in the same engine room, which drove by gearing, and the new engine had to be placed the opposite way to secure room for the rope drive. The mill closed in the early 1960s. A Lumb governor was fitted, probably in the 1920s.

98. Rochdale, Rochdale Steam Laundry, Manchester Road   SER 1184

Type:	Horizontal single cylinder non-condensing
Photo taken:	1965
Maker and Date:	J. Petrie & Co., Rochdale? 1890s
Cylinder/dimensions:	12in x 2ft 0in – slide valve
Hp: 40	*Rpm:* 100 *Psi:* 120
Service:	Main drive by 9in belt off rim of 5ft 6in flywheel.

This certainly ran for over sixty years, driving the plant and heating the water from the exhaust steam, and was a plain simple unit that could not have been bettered for the service. It was designed as a general service adaptable engine, having provision for drive off either side, i.e. there was a facing to allow a crankshaft bearing on the nearer side had the drive been needed there. It probably never had a breakdown or major repair in its lifetime. Laundry closed and scrapped in 1970?

99. Rochdale, Schofield, Ltd., Buckley Mill   SER 175

Type:	McNaughted single beam
Photo taken:	1936
Maker and Date:	Petrie & Co., Rochdale, 1863
Cylinder/dimensions:	$30^1/_2$in x 5ft 6in – slide valve
	$22^1/_2$in x 2ft 9in – piston valve
Hp: 300	*Rpm:* $42^1/_2$ *Psi:* 120
Service:	Woollen mill. Gear drive off flywheel arms. Flywheel 16ft 0in diameter.

This was built at the Whitehall Street Works, and started in 1864, powering the Old and the New Mills, driving the latter by a 4in shaft under the mill road. It was McNaughted by Petrie in 1896, and in later years was developing 92 hp in the high pressure cylinder and 160 in the low pressure. The flywheel weighed thirty tons, the spur gear ring on the arms having teeth $8^1/_2$in wide x 3in pitch. The crankshaft was 10in diameter, and a new crankpin was made in 1940 by Webbs & Bury, and fitted by the Ebor Co. The beam broke in 1916 and was only replaced when the original pattern was found. The engine was sold for scrap metal for £300 in 1963, and the mill demolished later, the works having closed in 1960.

100. Rochdale, Sparth Mill Co.   SER 591

Type:	Horizontal twin tandem condensing
Photo taken:	1953
Maker and Date:	J. & W. McNaught, St George's Foundry, Rochdale. 1901
Cylinder/dimensions:	21³/₄ in and 42in x 5ft 0in each side – Corliss and piston valves
Hp: 1,600	*Rpm:* 68 *Psi:* 150
Service:	Cotton spinning. Flywheel 24ft diameter, 42 ropes.

This was probably little altered during its sixty years life during which it was certainly overloaded by at least 25%. It was called *Sparth*, and in later years a Lumb governor was fitted, and in 1953, two new steel boilers were installed which cost £2,000 each. It ran on, mule spinning until, in the 1950s, electrically driven ring spinning frames were gradually installed. Then one half of the engine was run for some years, and finally scrapped on completion of the ring frame programme. The mill was closed about 1967.

101. Rochdale, Standard Mill   SER 590

Type:	Twin tandem compound horizontal
Photo taken:	1953
Maker and Date:	J. & W. McNaught, St George's Foundry, Rochdale, 1890
Cylinder/dimensions:	26in and 46in x 6ft 0in each side – slide and piston valves originally
Hp: 2,000	*Rpm:* 43 *Psi:* 100-120
Service:	Cotton spinning. Flywheel 28ft diameter, 43 ropes.

The engines were built to develop 1,600 hp with steam at 100 psi, but when more carding machines were installed in 1912, at least 2,000 hp was needed, so new high pressure cylinders with McNaught drop valves were put in. These served until 1942, when increased production again being needed, the boiler pressure was raised to 120 psi, and power went up to 2,500 hp. The mill was turned over to electrical driving with its own diesel engined generators in 1955, and the steam engine was scrapped. It cost £4,000 in 1890.

102. Rochdale, Stott & Co., Mellor Street Mill   SER 719

Type:	Horizontal four cylinder triple expansion (was tandem compound)
Photo taken:	1955
Maker and Date:	Wood Bros., Sowerby Bridge, 1906 & 1911
Cylinder/dimensions:	13¹/₂ and 27in x 3ft 6in and 22in and 23in x 3ft 6in – Corliss valves
Hp: 700	*Rpm:* 95 *Psi:* 180
Service:	Cotton spinning and weaving.

This was built as a tandem compound of 400 hp in 1906 with cylinders of 13¹/₂ in and 27in bores, and was converted to triple expansion in 1911 by the addition of cylinders of 22in and 23in bore. The engine drove the spinning section only, weaving having always been electrically driven. The mill was running until about 1970, but may have closed after.

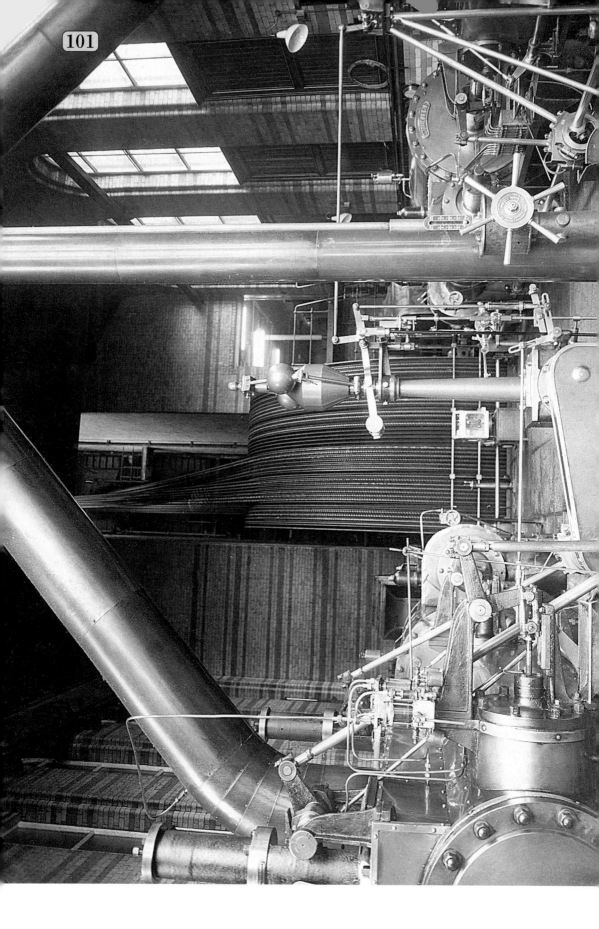

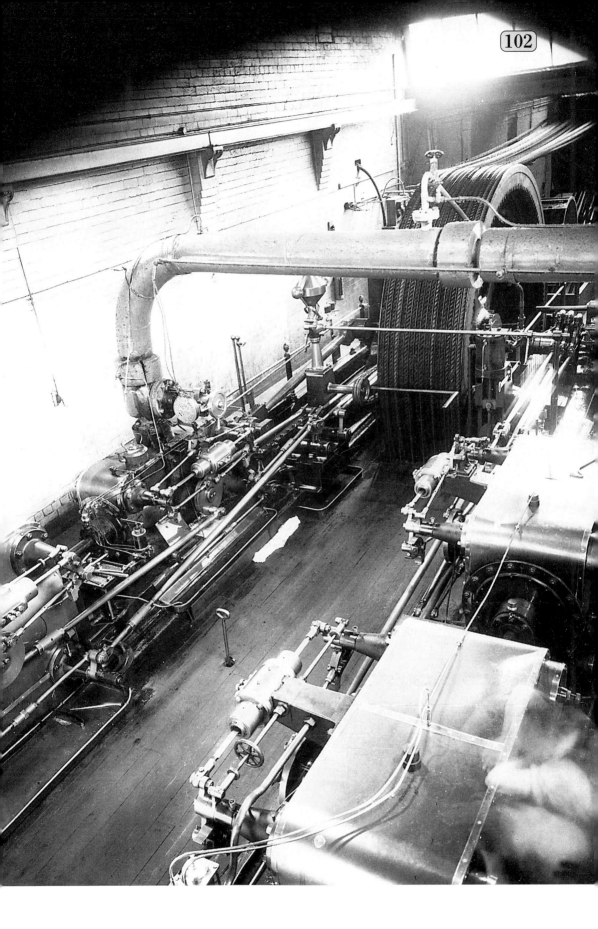

103. Rochdale, Victoria Mill Co., Woodbine Street   SER 760

Type:	Horizontal four cylinder triple expansion
Photo taken:	1955
Maker and Date:	J. & W. McNaught, St. George's Foundry, Rochdale, 1899
Cylinder/dimensions:	21¹/₂ in, 33, 37in and 37in bore x 4ft 6in – Corliss and piston valves

Hp: 1,200   *Rpm:* 71   *Psi:* 160
Service: Cotton spinning. 36 rope drive.

This was McNaught's standard mill design for triple expansion, with Corliss valves on the high, and piston valves on the intermediate and low pressure cylinders. All of the piston valves were of the twisting type, the twist for the intermediate cylinder on the left being provided from a cam, and the squared valve spindle, with the low pressure valves moved by diagonal links and ball-ended arms. The tubular piston valve rods were built up by welding in the 1950s, otherwise little was needed until the mill was closed in the cotton trade reorganisation of 1960.

104. Royton, Roy Mill Co.   SER 710

Type:	Horizontal twin tandem condensing
Photo taken:	1955
Maker and Date:	Buckley & Taylor, Oldham, 1906
Cylinder/dimensions:	22in and 44in x 5ft 0in each side – Corliss and slide valves
Hp: 1,600	*Rpm:* 70 *Psi:* 180
Service:	Cotton spinning. Rope drive.

This was unusual for the late date in that it was fitted with slide valves on the low pressure cylinders. It had remained as built however, and the five boilers still worked at the original 180 psi when fifty years old. The plant, developing full power, used about eighty tons of coal per week, costing £3.4.0. per ton in the 1950s. Although electrical power cost more, the mill was converted to motor drives and the engine scrapped. The mill was still running in the late 1960s.

105. Royton, Royton Ring Mill   SER 1131

Type:	Horizontal cross compound
Photo taken:	1963
Maker and Date:	Urmson & Thompson, Hathershaw Ironworks, Oldham, 1908
Cylinder/dimensions:	29in and 59in x 5ft 0in – Corliss valves
Hp: 1,700	*Rpm:* 67 *Psi:* 160
Service:	Cotton spinning. 36 ropes from 24ft flywheel.

The mill was unusual in that the engine was placed at a very high level, with the top floor drives almost horizontal, as the print shows. There were forty steps up to the engine room from the mill yard, whereas many mills had only six or eight. The engine room tiling was particularly fine, with moulded facings to the ceiling level, and around the window apertures. The tubular tail rod covers were very neat, and the finish everywhere was very good. The drives were gradually converted to motor driven ring spinning frames in the 1960s, and with all of the spinning thus, the preparation was completed by 1965 and the engine was then scrapped – a pity as it was a fine example of the later Lancashire finish.

106. Salford, J. Eaton & Co.   SER 1199

Type:	Horizontal single cylinder non-condensing
Photo taken:	1965
Maker and Date:	Daniel Adamson & Co., Dukinfield, 1888
Cylinder/dimensions:	16in x 3ft 0in – Semi rotary valves
Hp: 120	*Rpm:* 100 *Psi:* 100
Service:	Works drive by 12in belt to mainshaft. Fur manufacturers.

Daniel Adamson took out a licence to make Wheelock valves after seeing the engine exhibited in the 1884 Exhibition. Eaton's was the simplest type, with fixed cut-off and throttle governing. There were two semi-rotating valves below the cylinder, each with its own eccentric, but with a variable travel adjustment to alter the travel and cut-off in the inlet valve. It had the Wheelock type frame, and appeared to have had no alterations in the sixty two years it ran the plant, until motors were installed about 1960. There was no record of any breakdowns, and it was the last Adamson engine left as far as can be traced when it was removed about 1970. There were two boilers by Adamson. The little plant closed soon after possibly due to re-development of the area, which totally destroyed its character.

107. Salford, Seedley Bleach Works, later Croft Laundry   SER 1141

Type:	Single cylinder oscillating
Photo taken:	1963
Maker and Date:	Mather & Platt, Salford, 1870s?
Cylinder/dimensions:	Approx. 20in x 5ft 0in – slide valve
Hp: ?	*Rpm:* 10? *Psi:* 80
Service:	Well pump drive, direct to bell cranks of 2 pumps.

This comprised an oscillating cylinder coupled directly to the upper arm of one bell crank, with a connecting rod coupled to the crankshaft from a point half way down the bell crank arm. The steam was exhausted into the works process steam lines, at about 10 psi. The bell cranks had stroke of about 5ft, with a well pump on each. The well depth was not known, but the laundry water supply was secured from it by an electric submersible pump. A slide valve was fitted to the cylinder, and was operated by an eccentric and sliding block. It was dismantled about 1965-6.

108. Salford, Wadkin & King, Wellington Mill   SER 176a

Type:	Double beam with double pusher engines
Photo taken:	1937
Maker and Date:	Beam engine = Fairbairn? 1844
Cylinder/dimensions:	$30^{1}/_{4}$in & $33^{1}/_{4}$in x 6ft 0in – slide valves
Hp: ?	*Rpm:* 32 *Psi:* 5–10
Service:	Cotton doubling. Gear drives to four floors by vertical shaft. Flywheel had 241 teeth to 55 on mainshaft pinion. Beams 19ft 6in long; flywheel 21ft 0in diameter

This was technically interesting as the last working example of the Fairbairn layout, in which the engines ran at different speeds, and were coupled to the same mainshaft. The beam was identical with the illustrations in Bourne's *Steam Engine* of a Fairbairn beam (his works were nearby). The engine was unaltered. The works closed in c.1940.

109. Salford, Wadkin & King, Wellington Mill   SER 176b

Type: Double cylinder horizontal engine
Photo taken: 1937
Maker and Date: History unknown, c. 1860s?
Cylinder/dimensions: 20in & 20in x 3ft 6in – slide valves
Hp: -   *Rpm:* 54   *Psi:* 100
Service: Pusher engines geared to main shaft. Flywheel: 115 teeth;
                           pinion: 48 teeth

These were very massive engines, almost certainly dating from the 1860s with a heavy flywheel with a toothed rim. They were very plain and ran with very little trouble. The horizontal engine house was an additional building at the left hand side of the beam engine and the engine coupled to the mill by a short extension of the second motion shaft. There were two Lancashire boilers.

110. Salford, Wilson & Wilkinson & Co.   SER 750

Type: Twin cylinder quick reversing
Photo taken: 1955
Maker and Date: Armstrong, Whitworth, Newcastle upon Tyne, Date unknown
Cylinder/dimensions: 5in x 9in – Piston valves
Hp: *Rpm:*   *Psi:*
Service: Road rolling. Three shaft. Building contractors.

The tandem rollers were designed for tarmac rolling and so had to reverse instantly to avoid any tendency to form depressions at the end of the run before reversing. This was fitted with twin rear rolls with differential action in the chain drive from the second motion shaft and there was only one speed, and the engine was fitted with a sliding pinion to allow the engine to be run on its own, for boiler feeding. Regularly in use in the 1950s it was scrapped for a diesel engined roller later, after use in widely scattered areas.

111. Salford, Winterbottom Book Cloth Co.   SER 860a

Type: Horizontal cross compound
Photo taken: 1957
Maker and Date: George Saxon Ltd., Manchester, 1919
Cylinder/dimensions: 18in and 34in x 4ft 0in – Corliss valves
Hp: 400   *Rpm:* 40   *Psi:* 140
Service: Nos. 1 & 2 Mills. Drive by gearing.

This replaced an older engine, and the new house and engine were designed to drive a line of cloth polishing calenders, themselves a considerable load, and also to run a part of the new motor driven plant then installed. The drive was by gearing from the flywheel arms to a second motion shaft, and, after driving the alternator, the shaft continued through to the calender room to drive the 6 calenders (which are heavily pressed or loaded heated rollers which glazed the bookcloth by heat and friction) by the usual side shaft and bevel wheels. One of Saxon's latest jobs, the gearing and the engine were very good, giving little trouble until the whole was to go over to electric driving about 1960.

111

112. Salford, Winterbottom Book Cloth Co.   SER 860b

Type:	Inverted vertical compound
Photo taken:	1957
Maker and Date:	Scott & Hodgson, 1912?
Cylinder/dimensions:	$18^1/_2$ in and 30in x 3ft 0in – Corliss valves
Hp: Approx. 500	*Rpm:* 75 *Psi:* 140
Service:	Nos. 3 & 4 Mills. Drive by ropes to alternator.

This was possibly a new section of the works built at the time, but the history was very difficult to trace. The concern was old but always made a very good product, and with the heavy loads, plant wear was great, and re-modelling kept it efficient. The calenders were however best driven by the side shaft and bevel gear system since with all rarely at work at the same time, a smaller power was ample to drive the whole of a shop. With motors the power had to equal that of each machine despite incidence of usage.

113. Salford, Winterbottom Book Cloth Co.   SER 860c

Type:	Horizontal cross compound condensing
Photo taken:	1957
Maker and Date:	Unknown, c. 1870s?
Cylinder/dimensions:	20in and 40in x 4ft 6in – Corliss valves
Hp: Approx. 500	*Rpm:* 57 *Psi:* 140
Service:	Calendering shop drive.

Named *Archibald and Helen*, this was almost certainly built as a slide valve twin cylinder engine, possibly by Saxon, as the frame had some appearance of this. The Corliss valve cylinders were fitted by Saxon in 1915 when more power was needed, and other alterations had led to new boilers being installed. The drive was by gearing, with the driving wheel separate from the flywheel and staked on to the crankshaft. It drove two shafts one on either side of the room, by bevel gearing, one driving 8 and the other shaft driving 11 calenders, with a dog clutch to each machine. All was scrapped on the changeover to electrical drives in the 1960s.

114. Shaw, Briar Mill Co.   SER 1133

Type:	Horizontal four cylinder triple expansion
Photo taken:	1963
Maker and Date:	George Saxon Ltd., Manchester, 1907
Cylinder/dimensions:	25in, 38in, 42in and 42in x 5ft 0in – Corliss valves
Hp: 2,000	*Rpm:* 65 *Psi:* 180
Service:	Cotton spinning. 40 rope drive off flywheel approx. 24ft diameter.

Typical of Saxon's best work, Briar was one of the largest horizontals they made. The engine room was unusual in that the windows on either side were not identical but the finish and the upkeep of the engine were in the best Lancashire tradition. The only addition was the fitting of a Lumb governor system probably in the 1920s. The print shows it in its everyday condition. Replacement of the original mule spinning by motor driven ring frames proceeded gradually in the 1960s and with the load reduced to the preparation (as seen in the print) on the lower floor, the engine was very lightly loaded, (about 600 hp as seen). The changeover was finally completed in the mid-1960s and the engine was then scrapped. A feature of the mill itself was that the buildings were not of the same height on either side of the engine room.

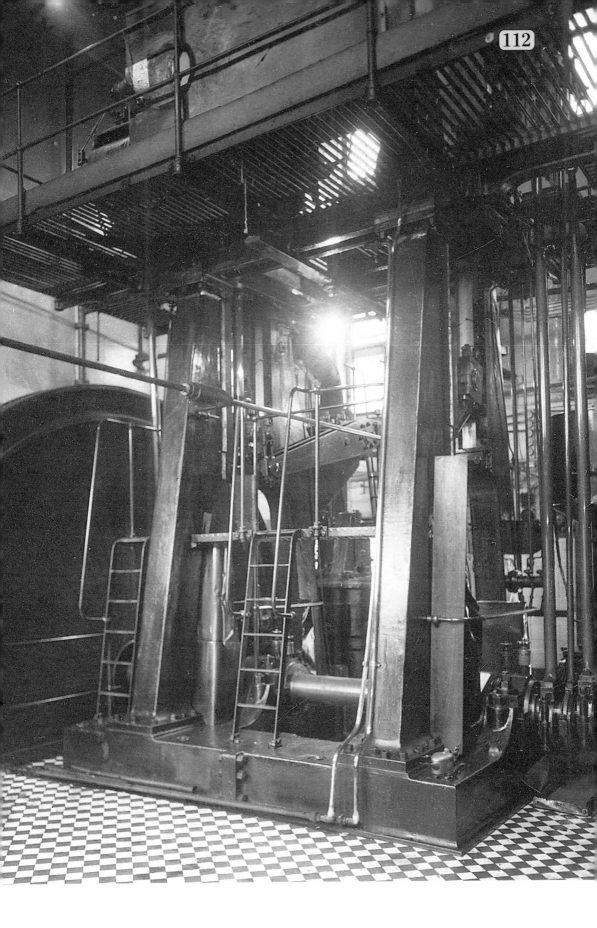

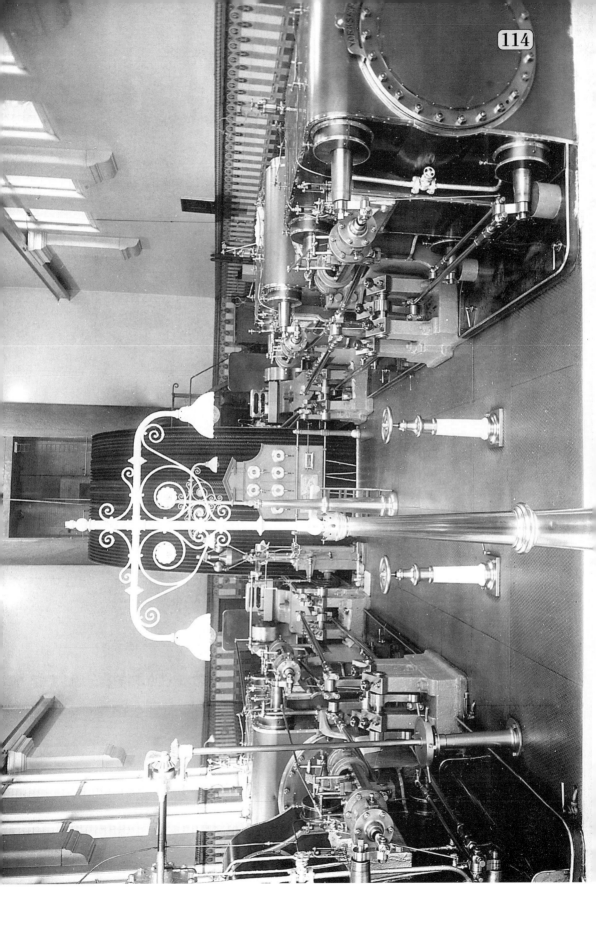

115. Shaw, Dawn Mill Co.   SER 601

Type:	Horizontal twin tandem compound
Photo taken:	1953
Maker and Date:	George Saxon Ltd, Manchester, 1902
Cylinder/dimensions:	20$^{1}/_{2}$ in and 40in x 5ft 0in each side – Corliss valves
Hp: 1,400	*Rpm:* 63 *Psi:* 160
Service:	Cotton spinning. Flywheel 26ft diameter. 35 ropes.

This was Saxon's usual design of which many were fitted into Lancashire spinning mills, and, a substantial design, required little attention until the mill was closed in the late 1960s. The Tetlow boilers were interesting as they had the maker's name upon a cast iron frame around the top of the boiler shell at the front.

116. Shaw, Fitton & Co., Shaw Side Mill   SER 502

Type:	Double McNaught beam
Photo taken:	1952
Maker and Date:	Buckley & Taylor, Oldham, 1880
Cylinder/dimensions:	33in x 3ft 0in and 36in x 6ft 0in – slide valves
Hp: 1,200	*Rpm:* 34 *Psi:* 120
Service:	Cotton spinning.

A typical heavy Oldham type engine, this latterly carried a heavy overload. The gear drives to the mill buildings passed underground as well as by vertical shafts, but as the mill was highly productive, the gearing must have been well maintained otherwise friction losses would have been excessive. It was probably the last remaining large beam engine which had not had Corliss valve cylinders fitted in the early 1900s. One high pressure cylinder was fractured by water entering it in 1951, and the engine ran on one side only until this was replaced. The drawings were prepared by Frank Wightman from the broken pieces, the cylinder being cast and machined by Stott of Haslingden, and fitted by Whittakers of Oldham. A similar failure occurred some years later, and after running on one side again, the mill was closed and all scrapped in a period of poor trade. It was the last of the older heavy Oldham beam engines.

117. Shaw, Hardman, Ingham & Co., Diamond Rope Works   SER 1352

Type:	Inverted vertical compound condensing
Photo taken:	1968
Maker and Date:	Scott & Hodgson, Guide Bridge, 1912
Cylinder/dimensions:	14in and 30in x 2ft 6in – Corliss and piston valves
Hp: 250?	*Rpm:* 90 *Psi:* 160
Service:	Works drive. 14 ropes off 10ft 0in flywheel.

This was a very neat works, always well kept, and busy until a serious fire destroyed the mill itself in 1972, although the engine was unharmed. The damage caused the concern to close and the engine remained in situ when new owners took over the premises for another trade. It is hoped that it will be saved, as it is the last but one vertical mill engine left, and is small and not too difficult to remove. The engine room was very confined, almost impossible to photograph adequately without a special lens. Publisher's note: this engine was in fact removed for preservation by the Northern Mill Engine Society in 1995.

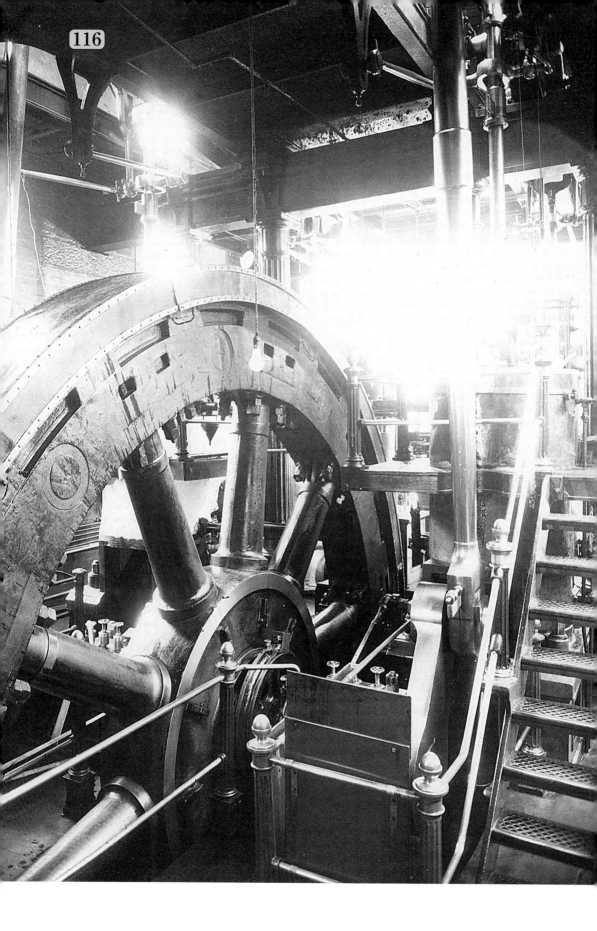

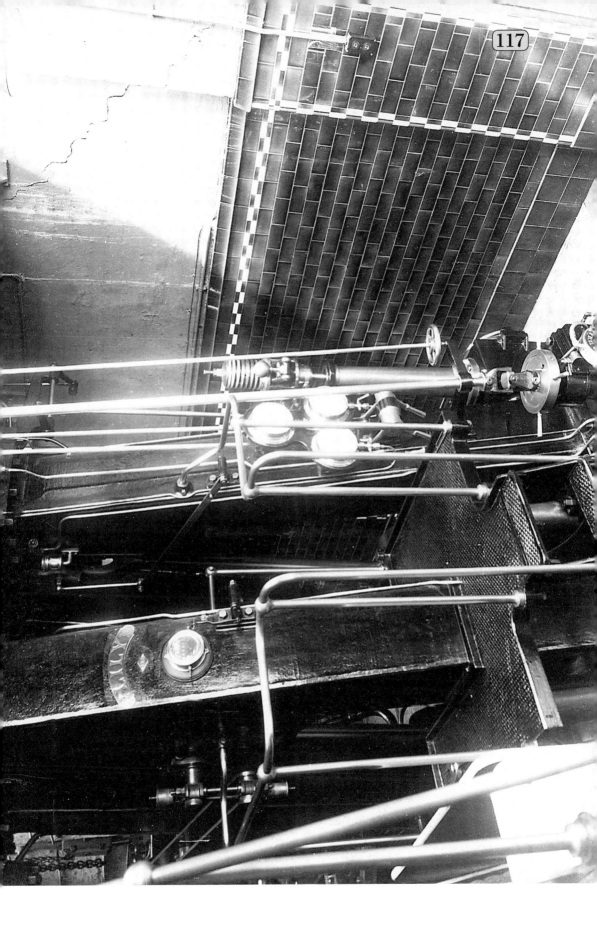

118. Shaw, J. Milne & Co., Clough Mill   SER 792

Type:	Horizontal side by side compound condensing
Photo taken:	1956
Maker and Date:	Buckley & Taylor, Oldham, 1911
Cylinder/dimensions:	15in and 32in x 3ft 0in – Corliss and slide valves
Hp: 290	*Rpm:* 77 *Psi:* 160
Service:	Waste cotton spinning. Rope drives to two mill blocks.

A beam engine had driven the original block, and possibly when a new company took over, a new mill block was added and this engine was made to drive the two sections, and probably placed near to the old engine room. The old side took 150 hp alone, and with the new as well the load was 293 hp. The engine continued to drive the whole until electrical drives were installed in the late 1950s, and the engine scrapped. The rope drives were concealed in a separate race and not easy to check, but there were only 8 or 9 ropes at the most.

119. Shaw, Fern Mill, latterly Sutcliffe, Speakman & Co.   SER 1227

Type:	Horizontal twin tandem compound
Photo taken:	1966
Maker and Date:	Buckley & Taylor, Oldham, 1884
Cylinder/dimensions:	22in and 44in x 6ft 0in – Corliss and slide valves
Hp: Approx. 1,200	*Rpm:* 54 *Psi:* 150
Service:	Grinding mills for carbon black. Geared drive.

This was Buckley & Taylor's standard engine for the heavily loaded coarse count cotton mills of the 1880s. These were built with slide valves on the high as well as the low pressure cylinders for steam at 100 psi and drove to vertical shafts by spur teeth on the flywheel rim. Most of these engines were rebuilt in the early 1900s, with Corliss valve high pressure cylinders, and new boilers for 160 psi which reduced the fuel used, and made the older mills competitive with the newer ones. The left-hand engine was christened *Oldham* and the right-hand one *Crompton*. The mill ran well on mule cotton spinning until 1939, when it closed under the Government concentration scheme. The plant was retained, but it never worked on cotton spinning again. It was however purchased by Sutcliffe, Speakman and Co. in 1951, and the engine was then used to drive ball-type colour grinding mills for some twenty-seven years, when the crankshaft broke, and electrical driving then had to be adopted.

120. Smallbridge, nr. Rochdale, Law's Chemical Works   SER 1453

Type:	Inverted vertical single cylinder
Photo taken:	1973
Maker and Date:	E. S. Hindley, Bourton, Dorset, c. 1890
Cylinder/dimensions:	3in x 5in – slide valve
Hp: 2	*Rpm:* 120 *Psi:* 100
Service:	Plant for mixing chemicals for the textile trade.

A small works started in the 1890s, preparing a wide variety of special chemical fluid mixtures, largely for the finishing side of the textile trade. It has kept going on sound products, and good service with a very small staff and with all of the manufacturing plant in a room 50ft x 20ft. The vertical centre flue boiler of 1953 by Farrars of Newark – 3ft diameter x 7ft 6in high, supplies steam at 100 psi for heating the mixtures, as well as to drive the small engine which drives the agitators in a large mixing vat, its sole duty. The exhaust steam is used for water heating. The finished products are sent out in drums and the engine is used twice weekly for the various mixings. The engine base is circular 14in diameter, and other than some new bearings and recent overhaul work by Glyn Jones of Todmorden, it is probably unaltered. There is no question of its replacement and it is well kept considering the work of the plant.

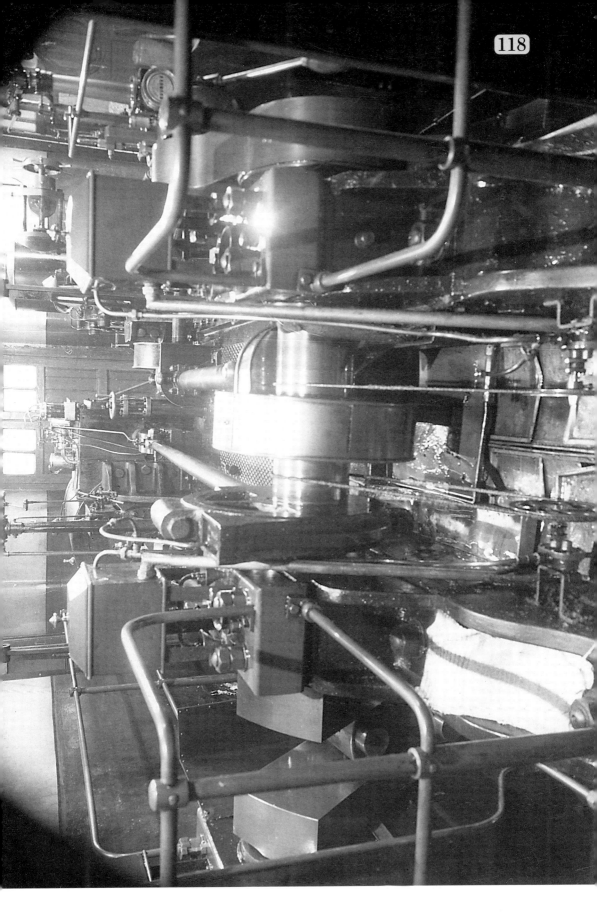

121. Southport, Southport Water Board, Bickerstaffe Pumping Station
SER 1004

Type:	Two single cylinder condensing beam
Photo taken:	1959
Maker and Date:	Yates & Thom, Blackburn, 1912
Cylinder/dimensions:	30in x 6ft 0in – piston valves
Hp: Approx. 100	*Rpm:* 20 *Psi:* 660
Service:	Town supply by two 18in ram pumps. 1 million gallons per day each, 180ft head.

These were almost certainly the last beam engines made by Yates & Thom and were in service for over forty years. They were lightly built with two surface ram pumps driven from the beams, which were of steel plate. Internal cut off valves were fitted to the steam cylinders and there were three boilers installed. These had also driven other steam plant, but only one beam engine remained in the 1960s; the load had long been taken by motor driven pumps. The framing was unusual in that the columns were in two sections each with the upper part carrying the beam gudgeon pedestals as a separate casting bolted to the top of the side frames. They were probably scrapped in the early 1960s.

122. St. Helens (near), Sutton Manor Colliery
SER 1329

Type:	Horizontal cross compound
Photo taken:	1968
Maker and Date:	Yates & Thom, Blackburn, 1914
Cylinder/dimensions:	Approx. 28in and 52in x 5ft 0in – Corliss valves
Hp: ?	*Rpm:* 45 *Psi:* 150
Service:	Coal winding, now from 500 yards, was 900 yards. Tail balance ropes.

It is probable that several of the collieries in this area were sunk by one company which believed in the economy and value of the compound winding engine, as there were other pits in the area which were fitted with them, whereas there were very few other cross compounds in this service in the entire country. Certainly they did very well at Sutton Manor, and Astley Green, also at Hatfield in Yorkshire. At Sutton Manor, rapidity and certainty of starting was assured by fitting a large receiver between the high and the low pressure cylinders, which was maintained at a pressure of 35 psi, by live steam fed in by a reducing valve, but this did not appear to supply much steam in coal drawing. Maintaining the receiver pressure assured a rapid start even if the low pressure crank only was in the effective position. The other winder at the pit was similar in design, but made by Fraser & Chalmers of Kent and there were three mixed pressure turbines and two Walker air compressors in use in 1972.

123. Trafford Park, Manchester, The Co-operative Wholesale Society, Sun Flour Mill
SER 749

Type:	Inverted vertical triple expansion
Photo taken:	1955
Maker and Date:	Yates & Thom, Blackburn, 1913
Cylinder/dimensions:	Approx. 25in, 40in and 60in x 4ft 0in – Corliss valves.
Hp: 2,200	*Rpm:* 85 *Psi:* 160
Service:	Mill drive by 38 ropes, and 22 to dynamo.

This was Yates and Thom's regular design, with all of the Corliss valves across the engine centre line, and massive cast iron columns for the front and back of the engine frame. It ran regularly for 6 days per week, and frequently ran for two years without bearing adjustments. It was still in very good condition when it was scrapped upon the changeover to electric motor drives in the late 1950s. There were also three Hick, Hargreaves inverted vertical compound enclosed Corliss valve engines designed for higher speeds and running with releasing cut-off valve gear under governor control, driving three dynamos for electrically driven plant around the mills. All was in full use in 1953, but was changed over a few years later to Grid current supply, and the steam plant scrapped.

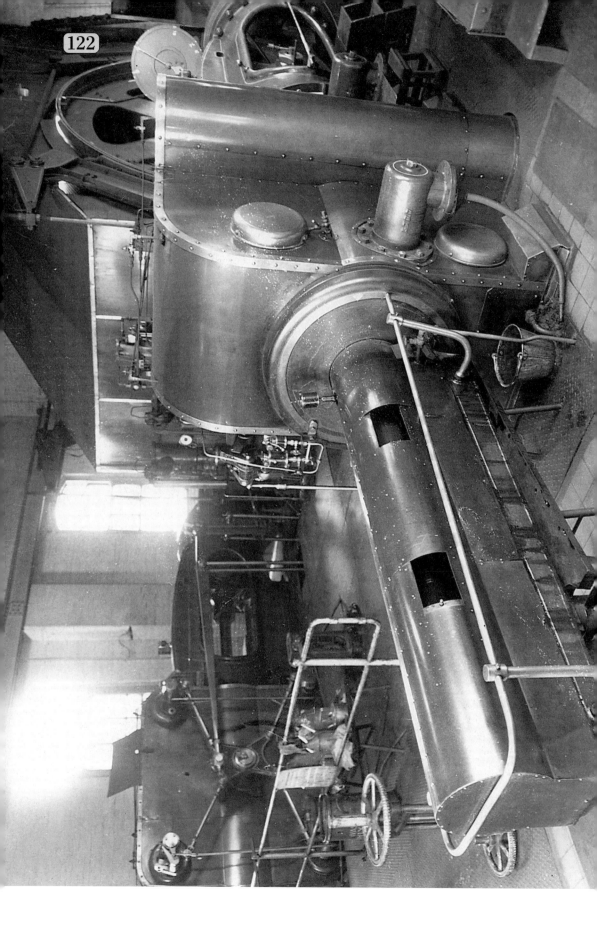

124. Trafford Park, Manchester, Corn Products Ltd.   SER 726

Type:	Horizontal single cylinder non-condensing.
Photo taken:	1955
Maker and Date:	Hick, Hargreaves & Co., Bolton, 1911
Cylinder/dimensions:	39in x 4ft 0in – Corliss valves.
Hp: 1,000	*Rpm:* 77 *Psi:* 100
Service:	Mill driven by ropes to generators.

This ran continuously day and night for over half a century, generating power and exhausting to the mill heating services at 6psi, the product requiring much low grade heat for boiling. It was very well kept and regularly overhauled, but was replaced when the whole of the power supply was reorganised, new water tube boilers replaced the 12 Lancashire ones, and a turbine generator installed for the increased power needs. The engine was certainly a very efficient unit, and possibly one of the last large ones to work in this way.

125. Trafford Park, Manchester, Taylor Bros., Wheel and Tyre Forge   SER 1389

Type:	Three horizontal three cylinder compound.
Photo taken:	1969
Maker and Date:	Lamberton & Co., Coatbridge, 1923
Cylinder/dimensions:	34in, 28in and 34in x 3ft 0in – piston valves.
Hp: 200 each	*Rpm:* 120 *Psi:* 140
Service:	Tyre mill drives.

The tyres were made from plain steel circular blanks, which, heated, were first pierced in the steam hammer to expand them into rings. These were then taken to the forging rolls driven by the engines, which in three stages rolled tyres of varying sizes to complete blanks ready for turning to size. The whole sequence of operations of three hammerings with varying dies to make the rough hollow blank, and then passing to finish in the three tyre mills driven by the engines, was completed in 4 minutes without reheating, with a team of some 15 men. It was very efficient in every way, with the hot metal manipulated mechanically throughout. On Nationalisation of the steel industry the whole was closed and tyre making transferred to the Rotherham mills where, with complete mechanisation, a quarter of the men turned the same output. The Manchester works are abandoned (1973) and plant possibly scrapped.

126. Trawden, nr. Colne, Hopkinson & Co., Black Carr Mills SER 1025

Type:	Horizontal single tandem compound condensing.
Photo taken:	1960
Maker and Date:	Wm. Roberts, Phoenix Foundry, Nelson, 1871
Cylinder/dimensions:	13^1/$_2$ in and 26in x 4ft 0in – slide valves.
Hp: Approx 400	*Rpm:* 56 *Psi:* 120
Service:	Cotton weaving. 30in belt drive to shed shaft. Once 800 looms.

This was known to have had a belt drive as early as 1871, and the engine was little altered after that time. The power was probably increased when a new shed was added in 1900 which at a higher level was driven by a pair of spur gearwheels about 5 feet diameter. The added load was driven by installing a new boiler in 1912 with 120 psi pressure. Electrical driving was intended in 1960 when the engine was to be scrapped.

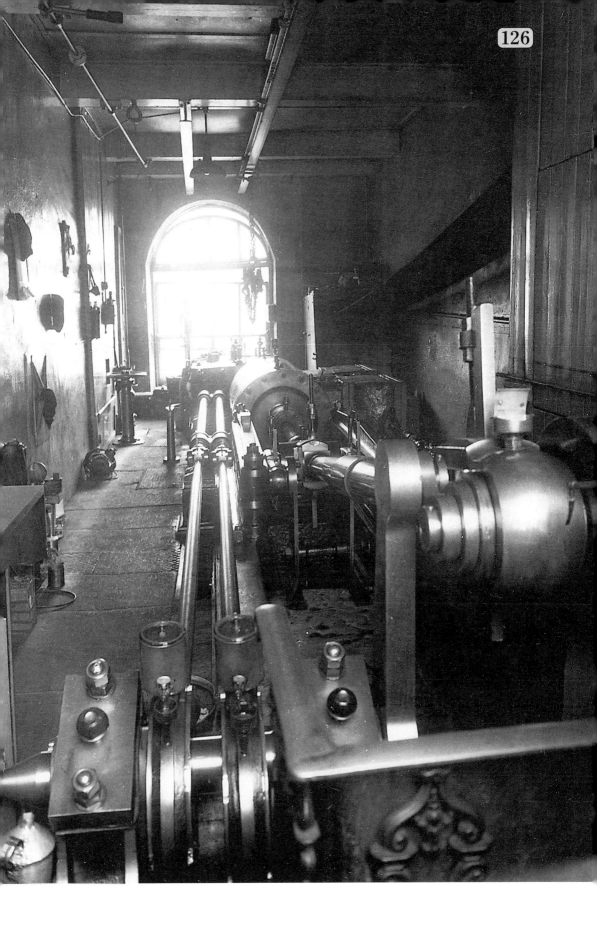

127. Turton, Thos Appleton & Co, Horrabin Mills   SER 264

Type:	Single cylinder beam.
Photo taken:	1939
Maker and Date:	Thompson & Cole, Bolton, 1845
Cylinder/dimensions:	36in x 7ft 0in – Slide valve.
Hp: 70	*Rpm:* 18 *Psi:* 18
Service:	Mill drive. Gear drive off flywheel rim to pinion.

This was completely as built, and in regular use in 1938 driving textile finishing plant by shaft and bevel gears to the machinery. The cap type beam ends, (i.e. the beam and piston rod and connecting rod gudgeons were mounted upon separate circular ends, and held to the beam by cotters) were an early feature, as was the long "D" slide valve, and the lattice eccentric rod. It was scrapped when the mills were closed.

128. Tyldesley, Astley Green Colliery (No. 1 shaft)   SER 642

Type:	Horizontal twin tandem non-condensing.
Photo taken:	1954
Maker and Date:	Yates & Thom. Blackburn, 1912
Cylinder/dimensions:	35in and 60in x 6ft 0in on each side – Corliss valves.
Hp: 3000 ?	*Rpm:* 20 *Psi:* 150
Service:	Coal winding. Shaft 2,500 ft deep.

Three engines were made to this specification; the other two went to Askern in Yorkshire. This engine wound over 9 tons of coal per wind from 850 yards, at its best in about $1^1/_2$ minute cycles. The output fell badly after Nationalisation, and despite modernisation, the pit was closed in 1970 and nearly all cleared, but the No. 1 engine has been preserved on site. The whole of the plant was steam driven, initially from the range of 15 Lancashire boilers.

129. Tyldesley, Astley Green Colliery (No 2 shaft)   SER 1353

Type:	Horizontal cross compound.
Photo taken:	1968
Maker and Date:	Yates & Thom, Blackburn, 1918
Cylinder/dimensions:	37in and 60in x 6ft 0in – Corliss valves.
Hp: ?	*Rpm:* 36 *Psi:* 160
Service:	Coal winding. Shaft 830 yds deep. Rope drum 11ft to 18ft diameter.

Astley Green was a late sinking, with both of the winding engines of the compound type but No.1 was a twin tandem compound. When winding coal this engine ran up to 36 rpm, and made up to 60 winds per hour. Steam was shut off after 12 of the 20 or so revolutions of the wind. There was an extensive power station, with three mixed pressure turbines generating electricity, and air compressing. There were 16 Lancashire boilers and latterly there was a high pressure boiler for 600 psi (D. Adamson, about 1960) and a turbine for this exhausting into the main steam lines. It was thus highly economical but despite the outlay the pit was closed.

130. Tyldesley, Gin Colliery   SER 691

Type:	Twin cylinder horizontal non-condensing
Photo taken:	1954
Maker and Date:	Possibly Teague & Chew, Cinderford? 1880?
Cylinder/dimensions:	26in x 4ft 6in – slide valves, with drop cut off.
Hp:	*Rpm:* *Psi:*
Service:	Coal winding. Rope drum 10ft 0in diameter.

This was nearly a century old when the pit was worked out and closed. There had been modifications to it as the tail rods had been removed and a steam brake added, and it was possible that the Teague cut-off gear was an addition, but little data was available at the colliery. The cut-off gear was effective and regularly used as it required a new bronze spiral adjusting sleeve in each side, which were made in the NCB workshops about 1952, despite the complex turning. All was scrapped when the seams were worked out in the later 1950s.

131. Tyldesley, Mosley Common Colliery   SER 1334

Type:	Horizontal double cylinder.
Photo taken:	1968
Maker and Date:	Fraser & Chalmers, Erith, No. 10755, 1905
Cylinder/dimensions:	36in x 5ft 6in – Corliss valves
Hp: ?	*Rpm:* 50 *Psi:* 120
Service:	Coal winding. Shaft 500 yards deep. Rope drum 18 ft diameter No.2 shaft.

Mosley Common was a great pit, with four shafts all steam wound, which was converted to electric winding in the mid 1960s and closed soon after in 1968. No.2 was a typical Fraser and Chalmers design; very neat and sturdy, and but for safety gear had little alteration. The colliery had good management and had adopted new machinery once it was proved. Major developments required a new chimney to be built in 1916 which may have been the start of the extensive electric power system with mixed pressure steam turbines, and in 1924, the largest air compressor built by Musgraves was installed. The other winders were made by Haigh Ironworks (No.4), Robey (No.3) and Greenhalgh (No.1). The pit was closed by 1968, and much, except the nearly new electric tower winder, was scrapped. In its full steam days there were three batteries of boilers, 22 in all, in use. The low pressure turbines were fed by the exhaust from Nos.2 and 4 winders and the air compressor later.

132. Tyldesley, Nook Colliery (No 4 Shaft)   SER 933

Type:	Horizontal twin cylinder.
Photo taken:	1958
Maker and Date:	J. Musgrave & Sons, Bolton. 1911
Cylinder/dimensions:	40in x 6ft 0in – drop and Corliss valves.
Hp: 1000	*Rpm:* 40 *Psi:* 120
Service:	No 4 shaft winder.

This was Musgrave's latest design of winding engine, and can be contrasted with the early design seen in SER 932. The trunk frame, tail rod guides, drop inlet valves, and general design, were all of the Continental type that Musgrave adopted in later years for their mill engines, and the trip gear was also of the mill type. The steam brake was original to the engine which, except for the slow banker, was very little altered. The steam cut-off point was under speed governor control, from a hydraulic cylinder to the cross shaft between the two cylinders, from which the trip steam cut-off gear was controlled. The engine room crane was an unusual refinement in a winding engine room. The pit was due for closure in the late 1960s.

133. Walkden, Newtown Colliery   SER 748(2)

Type:	Twin cylinder horizontal non-condensing
Photo taken:	1955
Maker and Date:	Clayton, Goodfellow, Blackburn, No.188-189, Date unknown
Cylinder/dimensions:	30 in x 5ft 0in – drop valves
Hp: ?	*Rpm:* 30 *Psi:* 100
Service:	Coal winding. No 2 shaft

There were many differences in the details of this. Thus the connecting rod was flattened at the sides, and the valves here were placed in each corner of the cylinder with the steam valves between the cylinders, controlled by the governor reducing the cut off point as the speed increased, yet leaving the engine under the driver's control at banking. The colliery was closed and the site cleared in the early 1960s. No. 2 engine had been fitted with a new drum, but otherwise was little altered.

134. Walkden, Newtown Colliery   SER 748

Type:	Twin cylinder horizontal non-condensing
Photo taken:	1955
Maker and Date:	Clayton, Goodfellow, Blackburn , No. 100 c. 1879?
Cylinder/dimensions:	30in x 5ft 0in – drop valves
Hp: ?	*Rpm:* 30 *Psi:*
Service:	Coal winding. No 1 shaft

This was the older of the two engines, the shafts having been sunk years apart. It retained the circular cast iron drum arms which Goodfellow often fitted to winders, and except for the addition of Daglish's patent steam cut-off gear, and later the fitting of overwinding and steam brake gear, was probably little altered over some eighty years of work. The cut-off gear on this engine was of the longitudinal cam bar type, not the usual toe and lifter type as on No. 2 engine.

135. Walkden, Edge Fold Colliery   SER 360

Type:	Non condensing Bull engine
Photo taken:	1950
Maker and Date:	Maker unknown, c.1840s
Cylinder/dimensions:	42in x 8ft 0in – piston valve
Hp: ?	*Rpm:* 6–8 *Psi:* 40
Service:	Pit pump. Shaft 330ft deep.

This was an old colliery site which was retained by the owners (Manchester Collieries) as a pumping and escape shaft for the adjacent collieries. This was a highly individual unit which operated with steam on the underside of the piston only and exhausted into an old egg-ended boiler as a silencer. Nothing was known of the engine's history, but some features were certainly those of a skilled and practical enginewright. It certainly worked very well, but was superseded by an electrically driven pump in the 1950s. It was curious that after many years of unexceptional service, it developed an unearthly groan in the last few weeks it was working, which could not be stopped by any method. Even NCB officials wondered; did it know its work was nearly done?

136. Walkden, Sandhole Colliery   SER 641(3)

Type:	Horizontal twin cylinder non-condensing
Photo taken:	1954
Maker and Date:	Worsley Mesnes Ironworks, Wigan, 1943
Cylinder/dimensions:	36in x 5ft 6in – piston valves
Hp:	*Rpm:* *Psi:*
Service:	Coal winding. No. 3 Pit.

This replaced a horizontal engine which had broken down, and was probably the last vertical shaft steam winding engine to be installed in the U.K. It was very neat and well finished, and may have been in stock at the works, certainly there was nothing of war-time austerity about the finish anywhere. It was the main coal drawing engine in later years, but together with all the plant, was scrapped when the pit was shut.

137. Walkden, Sandhole Colliery Nos 1 & 2 pits   SER 641

Type: Pithead buildings
Photo taken: 1954
Maker and Date: Unknown; 1866

The engine house held two vertical engines, made by J. Nasmyth of Manchester in 1866. The pits were to the left and right of the print, and the boilers were behind. The engines were twin cylindered, 30in x 5ft, one driving a winding drum of 12ft, the other of 13ft. They had slide valves with link motion reverse. Speeds were up to 30 rpm. In addition there was a single cylinder Nasmyth engine, 18in x 2ft 6in which drove a capstan. The engine house had brick walls with the internal drum walls of ashlar stone. The site was cleared in about 1963.

138. Walkden, Walkden Spinning Co.   SER 835

Type:	Spinning mill buildings
Photo taken:	
Maker and Date:	
Cylinder/dimensions:	
Hp:	*Rpm:* *Psi:*
Service:	

This was typical of the later cotton mills built in the last great phase of expansion in the early 1900s. The five boilers were in the house near to the chimney, with the triple expansion inverted vertical engine in the house behind, driving by about forty five ropes to the mill floors. It was built with six floors and the top floor was added later, again driven by ropes from the engine flywheel. The original mill design did not provide for this and a space had to be cut out of the top of the rope race arch to allow the rise of the ropes to the top floor. The mill was closed in 1958, and demolished, and the ground sold.

139. Walton-le-Dale, nr. Preston, Gatty & Co.   SER 753

Type:	Middle breast water wheel
Photo taken:	1955
Maker and Date:	Unknown
Cylinder/dimensions:	12ft diameter x 8ft 0in wide
Hp:	*Rpm:* *Psi:*
Service:	Works drive. Textile finishers

Probably dating from about 1860, this was in use driving a part of the works until 1939. The drive was by an internal toothed ring to a single mill pinion, and the arms were of timber, with an iron rim and buckets, but the sole plate was of elm. It was probably scrapped in the 1960s after long disuse. Gatty's began business on the site in 1886.

140. Wardle, nr Rochdale, Leach's Crossfield Woollen Mills   SER 365

Type:	Double beam compounded
Photo taken:	1951
Maker and Date:	Unknown – c. 1840's ?
Cylinder/dimensions:	21in and 30in x 3ft 6in – slide valves.
Hp: Approx. 100	*Rpm:* 40 *Psi:* 100
Service:	Mill drive by gearing

No history of the plant was known but the business was believed to have started in the 1840s, with the engine a double cylinder of about 30in bore. This ran for some fifty years when probably new boilers were needed, and it was then decided to install higher pressure boilers and make it compound by replacing one cylinder with a smaller high pressure one. After standing for many years the engine is being preserved by the Northern Mill Engine Society.

141. Warrington, Armitage & Rigby Ltd., Cockhedge Mills   SER 608a

Type:	Twin tandem compound horizontal
Photo taken:	1953
Maker and Date:	J & E Wood Ltd., Bolton, 1877
Cylinder/dimensions:	22in and 40in x 5ft 0in each side – Corliss valves
Hp: 1,300	*Rpm:* 46 *Psi:* 120 superheated
Service:	Cotton spinning. 3 belts off 28 ft flywheel.

This was unusual for the nearly vertical belt drive, which although rare was probably adopted when rebuilding after a serious fire in the 1870s. The Wood's high pressure cylinders were replaced by Scott and Hodgson in 1893, possibly when new boilers were needed, as the shed engine (SER 608b) was altered about then. The low pressure cylinders were unaltered, and retained the oscillating dash pots on the Corliss valve gear. The drives to the mill were originally all by belts, later partly changed to ropes, but finally replaced by about 70 electric motors of 1350 hp.

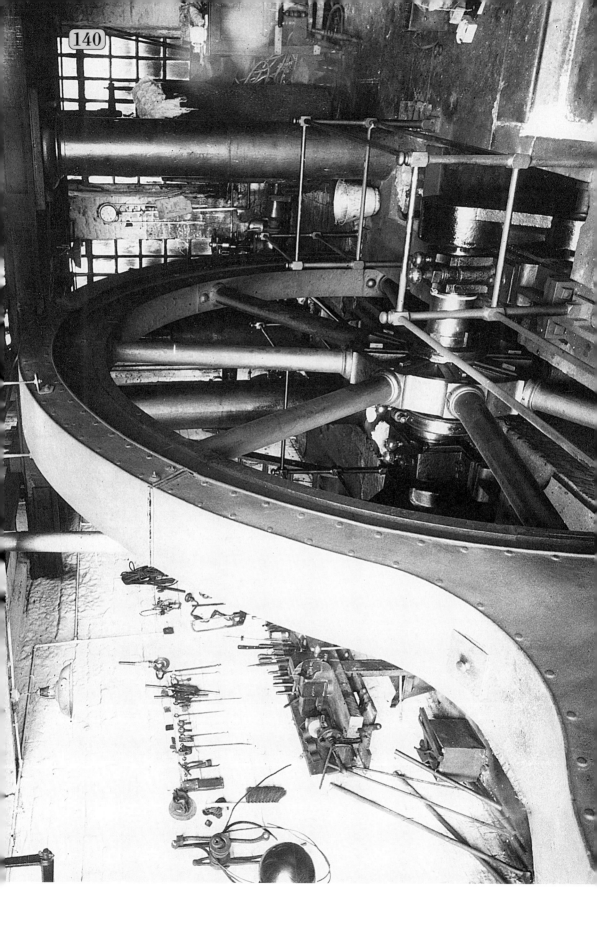

142. Warrington, Warrington Waterworks, Delph Lane Pumping Station

SER 607

Type:	Two Leavitt type bell crank triple expansion
Photo taken:	1953
Maker and Date:	No. 1 Jas. Simpson & Co., 1902. No. 2 Daglish & Co., St Helens, 1914
Cylinder/dimensions:	15in, 20in and 42in x 3ft 6in – Corliss valves
Hp: Approx 150	*Rpm:* 18 *Psi:* 160
Service:	Town water supply. Well to reservoir. Pump driven directly from the bell cranks below.

The piston rods drove through the bell cranks to the pumps directly below the engines, with a drive to the crank from the bell crank to steady the loading. There were two well and two forcing pumps to each engine. Although made by different makers the engines were in fact identical. The steam plant was replaced later by electrically driven sets, as the load greatly increased.

143. Whalley, Longworth & Co., Judge Walmsley Mill   SER 1098

Type:	Horizontal single tandem
Photo taken:	1962
Maker and Date:	Furnevall & Co., Haslingden, 1878
Cylinder/dimensions:	18in and 34$\frac{1}{2}$ in x 5ft 6in – Corliss and slide valves
Hp: 600	*Rpm:* 60 *Psi:* 160

The concern was founded in the 1850s with a beam engine driving one weaving shed, and the above engine almost certainly came from the Clough Shed, Barnoldswick in 1900, when a further shed was added at Longworths. It was built as a single cylinder condensing engine with the air pump at the rear of the low pressure cylinder. The high pressure Corliss valve cylinder at the rear, was an addition, having a separate bed fitted to the rear of the air pump framing, and was probably added when installed at Longworths to give the extra power needed by the added shed. It then ran on steam at 120 psi and was 24in bore, and had to be reduced by a liner to 18in bore when the new boiler for 160 psi was installed in 1934.

144. Whittle-le-Woods, Lawrence Cotton Ltd., Swansey Shed SER 798

Type:	Horizontal cross compound condensing
Photo taken:	1956
Maker and Date:	Victor Coates & Co., Lagan Foundry, Belfast, 1891
Cylinder/dimensions:	20in and 40in x 4ft 6in – Corliss valves
Hp: 500	*Rpm:* 45 *Psi:* 160
Service:	Cotton weaving.

This remained unaltered except for a new high pressure cylinder by Clayton, Goodfellow possibly in the early 1920s. It is probable that the boiler pressure was raised at the time, and it was in regular use until the shed was closed in the depressed conditions of the reorganisation programmes of 1959-60. Only a few Coates engines were used in Lancashire, and this, except for the high pressure cylinder, was unaltered. New main drive gearing was also supplied by Claytons, and this suggests that, as so often, the plant had long been over-loaded. The wooden cylinder lagging was attractive, and the single slipper crosshead guides were rarely used for large engines by the Lancashire engineers. All was scrapped at the closure.

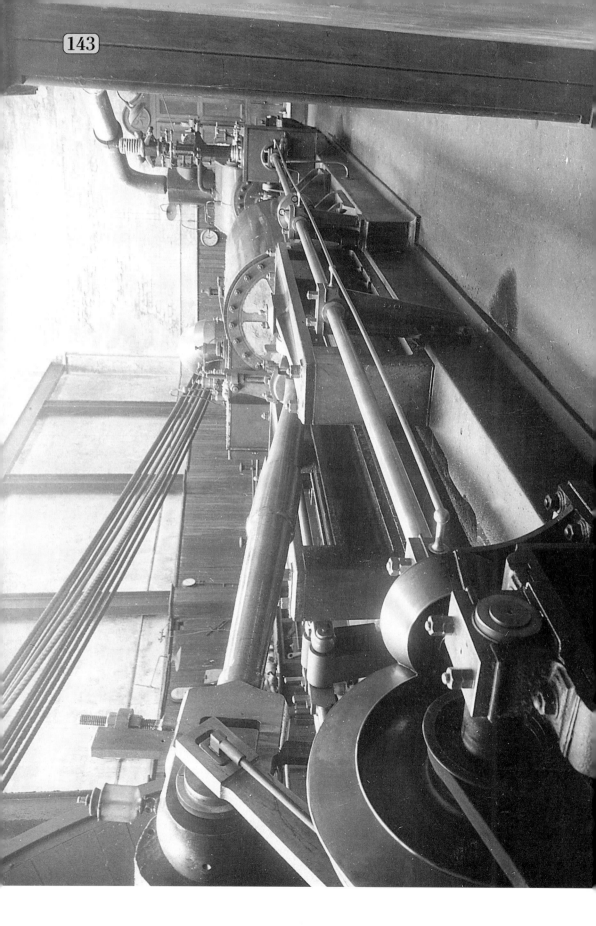

145. Whitworth, nr Rochdale, Facit Mill   SER 898

Type:	Horizontal cross compound
Photo taken:	1956
Maker and Date:	J. & W. McNaught, St George's Foundry, Rochdale
Cylinder/dimensions:	27in and 57in x 5ft 0in – Corliss valves
Hp: 1,500	*Rpm:* 65 *Psi:* 160
Service:	Cotton spinning. 30 rope drive.

This was the only low pressure cylinder of the design which McNaughts made and this was also their largest cylinder. The low level central layshaft for the valve gear drive was well out of the way, in contrast to some of the later engines of Oldham which had the cross shaft quite high, requiring steps to cross it. Lumb governing was fitted at a later date, but otherwise there was little but routine attention needed during its lifetime. Facit was outstanding in that there was no condensing water cooling lodge, there being a very large tank in the basement, possibly with spray coolers at the rear. There was no room on the site for a lodge as the hill rises directly from the back of the mill. Electric drives were installed in the rope race in 1957 and the engine scrapped.

146. Whitworth, nr Rochdale, Hall Fold Raising Co.   SER 874

Type:	Horizontal single tandem condensing.
Photo taken:	1957
Maker and Date:	J Petrie & Co., Rochdale, c. 1875
Cylinder/dimensions:	17in and32in x 3ft 6in – piston valves
Hp: 400	*Rpm:* 85 *Psi:* 120
Service:	Textile finishing plant, drive by 8 ropes.

Called *Elaine* this was typical of Petrie's design before they adopted Corliss valves. It almost certainly replaced a beam engine in the same room, and remained as built, even retaining the original governor. It was probably removed from the old Facit mill when the new large mill (See 898) was built in 1905. The piston valves were both of the plain twisting type, with Dowell cut-off control from the governor for the high pressure cylinder. Conversion to electric drives was in hand in 1957.

147. Wigan, Eckersleys Ltd   SER 983a

Type:	Non dead centre quadruple expansion
Photo taken:	1959
Maker and Date:	John Musgrave & Sons Ltd., Bolton, 1894
Cylinder/dimensions:	$14^1/_2$ in, $20^1/_2$ in,29in and 40in x3ft 6in – Corliss valves.
Hp: 1,000	*Rpm:* 80 *Psi:* 200
Service:	Cotton spinning. The "Old" or "Little" Mill. 22 rope drive.

Eckersleys were a very large concern latterly with six mills, with five boiler plants and chimneys, and this was one of the oldest mills left in 1954. There was a beam engine and gear drives until 1894, when this engine was installed. The load was heavy, as beside a spinning mill there was a weaving shed requiring some 700 hp at times, but the 22 rope drive would carry about 1200 hp maximum. It was unusual to leave spinning mill flywheel arms without casing, as wind drag could lose up to 50 hp, but this, apparently, was never cased in. It was a Musgrave standard non-dead centre type with triangular connecting rod. The concern greatly reduced its capacity as cotton spinning fell off, and by 1970 only two of the mill buildings were to remain, but the modern mills have high capacity with three shift working.

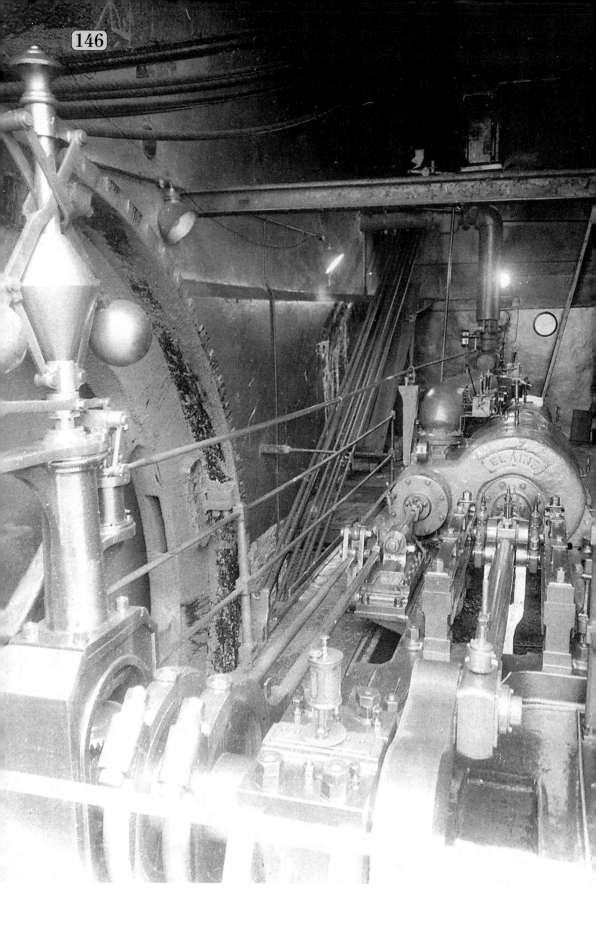

148. Wigan, Eckersleys Ltd.(No 2 Mill)   SER 983c

Type:	Horizontal cross compound
Photo taken:	1959
Maker and Date:	J & E Wood , Bolton, 1888
Cylinder/dimensions:	26in and 56in x 6ft 0in – Corliss valves
Hp: 1,500	*Rpm:* 53 *Psi:* 180
Service:	Cotton spinning. No 2 or Western Mill. 32 rope drive off 30ft flywheel.

This was J. & E. Wood's standard engine, but had new valve gear fitted by Musgrave in 1922. It was considerably damaged when a cotter in the low pressure connecting rod broke and among other repairs the fractured bed was strapped; the bed was certainly very shallow, only 16in deep. It was fitted with new boilers for 180 psi and superheat in 1910, and like all of Eckersley's engines was fully loaded for most of its life until 1950. The steam plant, and possibly the mill buildings, were dispensed with in the reorganisation of the late 1960s.

149. Wigan, Thomas Taylor, Victoria Mills   SER 609b

Type:	Inverted vertical cross compound
Photo taken:	1953
Maker and Date:	John Musgrave & Sons Ltd., Bolton. Date Unknown
Cylinder/dimensions:	28in and 58in x 4ft 0in – Corliss valves.
Hp: 2,000	*Rpm:* 76 *Psi:* 150
Service:	Cotton spinning and weaving. Load on this mostly weaving.

This was an old site, with many modifications, which had led to a great deal of gearing being added to connect drives to parts which had once had separate engines, there were in fact 5 pairs of bevel wheels carrying the drive to the main weaving shed. This was to be altered in 1954 when the other engine, a Scott and Hodgson of 2,000 hp of 1914 was to drive an alternator, with 5 new boilers, when the saving in frictional loss was calculated to eliminate the need for one engine entirely.

150. Wigan, Thomas Taylor, Victoria Mills   SER 609b (2)

Type:	Drives to loom shafts
Photo taken:	
Maker and Date:	
Cylinder/dimensions:	
Hp:	*Rpm:* *Psi:*
Service:	

This was the traditional weaving shed loom shaft drive, i.e. a main shaft along the side of the shed with bevel wheels at about 10ft 6in centres driving the shafts over the looms. It was usual to drive two pairs of looms by sloping belts from a group of pulleys placed close together, the shafts being progressively reduced in diameter as fewer looms remained to be driven down the shaft.

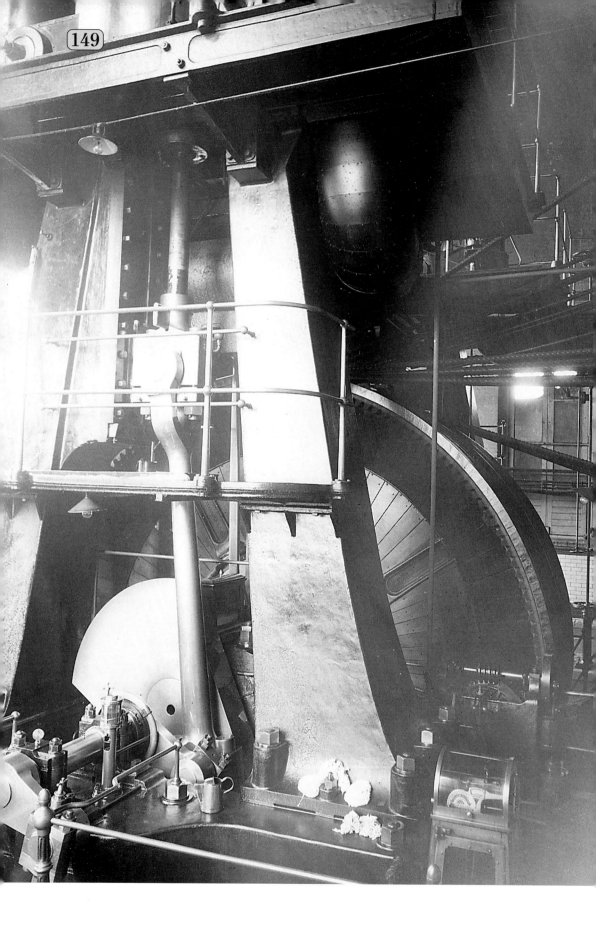

 # SERIES EDITOR, TONY WOOLRICH

Tony was born in Bristol in 1938. He became interested in technical history in his school days, and has been a Member of the Newcomen Society for 40 years, for ten years of which serving as a sub-editor of the *Newcomen Transactions*. He is also a Member of SHOT (the Society for the History of Technology), ICOHTEC (the International Committee for the History of Technology) and the Somerset Archaeological and Natural History Society.

He trained as a craftsman in the engineering industry, and from 1970 has combined his craft and historical skills in modelmaking for museums and heritage projects.

He has also published books and articles on aspects of technical history and biography. A particular interest is industrial espionage of the 18th century. Another interest is 18th century and early 19th century technical books and encyclopaedias, in particular Rees's *Cyclopædia*, (1802-1819). He has been working on a biography of the engineer John Farey, jr (1791-1851) for the past 20 years.

Since 1989 he has been heavily involved cataloguing for the National Monuments Record, Swindon, the Watkins Collection on the Stationary Steam Engine. He is also a constant consultee to the Monuments Protection Programme of English Heritage.

Since 1994 he has been acting as a contributor to the New *Dictionary of National Biography* working on biographies of engineers and industrialists. He is a contributor to the forthcoming *Biographical Dictionary of Civil Engineers,* published by the Institution of Civil Engineers.

He has recently completed for Wessex Water plc a study of the water supplies of Bridgwater, Wellington (Somerset) and Taunton, and was part of the team setting up the company's education centres at Ashford (near Bridgwater) and Sutton Poyntz (near Weymouth).

Publisher's Note

Eagle eyed readers will no doubt notice that plate 35 in this book is the same as that produced as plate 97 in Volume 3.1. This is an error in the collection and the repeat is deliberate. To be honest, we did not realise that plate 97 was the wrong one at the time.

SUPPLEMENT STEAM 3.2

These engines should have been included in Volume 3.1

1. Ashton-under-Lyne, Texas Mill   SER 1134

Type:	Inverted vertical
Photo taken:	1963
Maker and Date:	George Saxon Ltd., Manchester, 1907, altered 1921
Cylinder/dimensions:	21in, 33in, 51in x 4ft 0in as built 28in, 33in, 51in x 4ft 0in rebuilt

Hp: 1,250 then 1,800   *Rpm:* 78   *Psi:* 170
Service: Cotton spinning. 28 ropes off 22ft flywheel.

Texas was built as a mule spinning plant, but the engine must have been fully loaded even then as it was a successful mill. The machinery was gradually changed over to ring spinning from 1952 onwards. The busy mill always had full order books, and the load greatly increased by 1921, when probably more carding had to be added, to use lower grade cotton. The engine was then hopelessly overloaded, and was taking steam all through the stroke in the high pressure cylinder. Mr. Saxon was called in to advise on this, and he recommended conversion to three cylinder compound, which increased the power and economy. The final result was that the preferred mean pressure was reduced by $33\frac{1}{3}$ %. The total power was increased so that an 80 hp lighting load was added, and the coal used was 18% less. It ran thus for well over forty years, a credit to the builders who also modified it.

2. Ashton-under-Lyne, Stuart Bros.   SER 1136

Type:	Horizontal single cylinder non-condensing
Photo taken:	1963
Maker and Date:	R. J. Stringer, Ashton-under-Lyne, 1870s
Cylinder/dimensions:	8in x 1ft 3in – slide valve

Hp: Approx. 20   *Rpm:* 120   *Psi:* 60
Service: Washed and cleaned engine room wiping cloths. Cleaning cloth laundry.

Stuarts was a small plant which cleaned the engine wiping cloths, and recovered the grease and oil in them, but the oil was difficult to sell later. Although so small, the plant laundered some 30,000 cloths per week when there were many engines in the mills, employing some twenty hands, and maintained 15,000 per week in the 1950s with ten hands. The trade almost entirely died out when ring frames replaced the engines and mule spinning. The engine exhaust was used to boil the cloths, which were then dried in a wringing machine resembling a mangle. The little plant probably closed in the 1960s.

3. Bacup, Acre Mill, Stacksteads   SER 698

Type:	Horizontal cross compound condensing
Photo taken:	1954
Maker and Date:	J. Petrie, Rochdale, 1909
Cylinder/dimensions:	$15\frac{1}{2}$ in and 30in x 3ft 6in – Corliss and piston valves

Hp: Approx. 400   *Rpm:* 80   *Psi:* 160
Service: Cotton weaving and spinning.

This shows Petrie's late design, with slipper guide instead of the earlier trunk frame, and the crab claw type Corliss gear with vertical dashpots under the floor. Few repairs had been needed, but one main bearing was replaced in the 1950s. The mill probably closed in the early 1960s, and all scrapped. It probably replaced a horizontal engine in the same engine room, as there appeared to have been little general alteration.

4. Burnley, Edmundson Ltd., Empire Mill, Rose Grove   SER 980

Type:	Horizontal cross compound
Photo taken:	1959
Maker and Date:	Burnley Ironworks Co., 1915
Cylinder/dimensions:	19in and 36in x 4ft 0in – Corliss valve
Hp: Approx. 800	*Rpm:* 80 *Psi:* 150
Service:	Cotton weaving. 17 rope drive.

This was probably the last engine that the Burnley Ironworks installed in the area, if indeed they made any more complete engines. The engineer, his father and grandfather had all been apprentices to the Ironworks, and the engine thus had the best attention all its life, and was in fine condition when scrapped with the whole plant when the mill closed about 1960. It was typical Burnley Ironworks' design of the later period with the central stand for the steam and condenser water control, and with all of the valves below; their earlier engines had the inlet valves on top of the cylinder. The condenser was at the rear of the low pressure cylinder.

5. Kirkby, St Helens Waterworks, Kirkby Pumping Station   SER 794

Type:	Inverted cross compound
Photo taken:	1956
Maker and Date:	R. Daglish & Co, St Helens No 890, 1890
Cylinder/dimensions:	
Hp:	*Rpm:* 12-16 *Psi:* 100
Service:	Town supply to reservoirs from well

The well pump drive was from the crossheads by side rods to the force lift plunger pumps beneath the engine room floor, the pumps being driven by beams off the lower crossheads, to the well which was to one side of the engine. Even by the best water-works standards, the finish was exceptional throughout, with considerable gilding and many parts picked out in attractive colours. The engine house was also fine, a castel-lated circular stone house with an equally attractive chimney. The steam plant was scrapped when electric pumps were installed.

6. Kirkby, St. Helens Waterworks, Melling Pumping Station   SER 937

Type:	Horizontal single tandem
Photo taken:	1958
Maker and Date:	Robinson & Cook, Atlas Foundry, St. Helens, 1903
Cylinder/dimensions:	20in and 40in x 5ft 0in – Corliss valves
Hp: 250	*Rpm:* 20 *Psi:* 150
Service:	Town supply from wells. $1^1/_2$ million gallons per day to 350ft head.

This ran continuously for months on end, and rarely stopped for overhauls until the load went to new wells and electric pumps in the early 1960s, the water load having grown very much. The flywheel was large, i.e. 25ft. diameter by 25 tons weight. The pumps were behind the engine, with the well pair operated from a tee bob, with two plunger surface lift pumps, one near the engine, and the other driven by side rods passing beside the well pumps to another ram pump at the rear, giving a balanced load on the engine. One of the surface lift ram pumps is seen at the extreme right of the photograph, also the crosshead for the side rods to the well and rear plunger pump. The steam plant was dismantled soon after the new plant went into commission. There were two boilers, one used at a time. The Corliss valve gear resembled Musgrave's.

ENGINE MAKERS INDEX

Manufacturer	Plate No	SER No
Adamson & Co., D	106	SER 1199
Armstrong, Whitworth	110	SER 750
Ashton, Frost & Co	13	SER 826a
Ashton, Frost & Co	66	SER 1185
Ashton, Frost & Co	76	SER 911
Ashton, Frost & Co	83	SER 907
Ashton, Frost & Co	84	SER 908
Bailey & Co., W H	68	SER 1415
Bracewell & Co	62	SER 1187
Buckley & Taylor	104	SER 710
Buckley & Taylor	116	SER 502
Buckley & Taylor	118	SER 792
Buckley & Taylor	119	SER 1227
Buckley & Taylor	22	SER 858
Buckley & Taylor	43	SER 497
Buckley & Taylor	44	SER 966
Buckley & Taylor	48	SER 363b
Buckley & Taylor	49	SER 363c
Buckley & Taylor	51	SER 504
Buckley & Taylor	52	SER 729b
Buckley & Taylor	53	SER 722
Burnley Ironworks	28	SER 916a
Burnley Ironworks	61	SER 1159
Burnley Ironworks	214	SER 980
Clayton, Goodfellow	133	SER 748 (2)
Clayton, Goodfellow	134	SER 748
Coates & Co., V	144	SER 798
Crook, T T	63	SER 862
Daglish & Co	64	SER 801
Daglish & Co	142	SER 607
Daglish & Co., R	15	SER 647
Ebor Engineering	40	SER 1287b
Ebor Engineering	7	SER 174
Fairbairn	108	SER 176a
Forrester, G	11	SER 99b
Fraser & Chalmers	131	SER 1334
Furneval & Co	143	SER 1098
Furneval, J	78	SER 103b
Galloway, W & J	17	SER 495
Galloway, W & J	3	SER 1331
Galloway, W & J	4	SER 1180
Harvey & Co	10	SER 99a
Hathorn, Davy & Co	8	SER 759

Manufacturer	Plate No	SER No
Hick, Hargreaves	55	SER 968a
Hick, Hargreaves	124	SER 726
Hindley, E S	120	SER 1453
Howard & Co	46	SER 364a
Lamberton & Co	125	SER 1389
Lancaster & Tongue	70	SER 1156a
Leese, J	77	SER 103a
Mather & Platt	107	SER 1141
Mather Dixon	12	SER 99c
Mc Naught, J & W	100	SER 591
Mc Naught, J & W	101	SER 590
Mc Naught, J & W	103	SER 760
Mc Naught, J & W	87	SER 899a
Mc Naught, J & W	25	SER 1030
Mc Naught, J & W	37	SER 599
Mc Naught, J & W	145	SER 898
Musgrave & Sons Ltd	14	SER 1092
Musgrave & Sons Ltd	24	SER 713
Musgrave & Sons Ltd	31	SER 169a
Musgrave & Sons Ltd	32	SER 169b
Musgrave & Sons Ltd	65	SER 906
Musgrave & Sons Ltd	147	SER 983a
Musgrave & Sons Ltd	132	SER 933
Musgrave & Sons Ltd	149	SER 609b
Musgrave & Sons Ltd	69	SER 1230
Musgrave & Sons Ltd	72	SER 1157
Parsons & Co	54	SER 968b
Petrie & Co., J	27	SER 631
Petrie & Co., J	38	SER 973
Petrie & Co., J	75	SER 1057
Petrie & Co., J	85	SER 899b
Petrie & Co., J	86	SER 594
Petrie & Co., J	90	SER 597
Petrie & Co., J	91	SER 1103
Petrie & Co., J	92	SER 938
Petrie & Co., J	94	SER 596
Petrie & Co., J	96	SER 970
Petrie & Co., J	97	SER 593
Petrie & Co., J	98	SER 1184
Petrie & Co., J	99	SER 175
Petrie & Co., J	146	SER 874
Petrie & Co., J	210	SER 698
Pickup & Knowles	39	SER 1287
Pollit & Wigzell	19	SER 361
Pollit & Wigzell	56	SER 709
Pollit & Wigzell	57	SER 709a
Roberts & Co., W	29	SER 977
Roberts & Co., W	30	SER 976
Roberts & Co., W	33	SER 704a
Roberts & Co., W	34	SER 704b
Roberts & Co., W	126	SER 1025
Robinson & Cook	214	SER 937
Robinson, J	59	SER 895

Manufacturer	Plate No	SER No
Rothwell & Co	9	SER 100a
Saxon Ltd., G	16	SER 496
Saxon Ltd., G	111	SER 860a
Saxon Ltd., G	114	SER 1133
Saxon Ltd., G	115	SER 601
Saxon Ltd., G	23	SER 1164
Saxon Ltd., G	26	SER 1005
Saxon Ltd., G	45	SER 717
Saxon Ltd., G	80	SER 643
Saxon Ltd., G	210	SER 1134
Scott & Hodgson	112	SER 860b
Scott & Hodgson	117	SER 1352
Scott & Hodgson	81	SER 644
Scott & Hodgson	82	SER 645
Sharples & Co., W	88	SER 876a
Simpson & Co	142	SER 607
Stott & Co	41	SER 965b
Stott, S S	79	SER 156
Stringer, R J	210	SER 1136
Sutcliffe & Co	5	SER 267
Teague & Chew	130	SER 691
Thompson & Cole	127	SER 264
Unknown	109	SER 176b
Unknown	113	SER 860c
Unknown	135	SER 360
Unknown	140	SER 365
Unknown	35	SER 804
Unknown	47	SER 364b
Unknown	6	SER 104
Unknown	73	SER 1414
Unknown	95	SER 831
Urmson & Thompson	105	SER 1131
Urmson & Thompson	42	SER 967
Wood, J & E	102	SER 719
Wood, J & E	1	SER 637
Wood, J & E	141	SER 608a
Wood, J & E	148	SER 983c
Wood, J & E	18	SER 470
Woodhouse & Mitchell	93	SER 720
Worsley Mesnes	136	SER 641 (3)
Yates & Thom	121	SER 1004
Yates & Thom	122	SER 1329
Yates & Thom	123	SER 749
Yates & Thom	128	SER 642
Yates & Thom	129	SER 1353
Yates & Thom	2	SER 1051
Yates & Thom	67	SER 1031
Yates & Thom	89	SER 876b
Yates, W & J	36	SER 917
Yates, W & J	60	SER 785

NON STATIONARY ENGINE MAKERS INDEX

Subject	Plate No	SER No
Drives to loom shafts, Victoria Mills, Wigan	150	SER 609b(2)
Engine Builder's Workshop	20	SER 849b
	58	SER 538
Pipe Maker's Bench	21	SER 1339
Sandhole Colliery Building	137	SER 641
Spinning Mill, Walkden	138	SER 835
Textile Printing Machine drives	71	SER 1156b
Water wheel, Radcliffe	74	SER 1417
Water wheel, Walton-le-Dale	139	SER 753
Weaving Shed	50	SER 1117

SUPPLEMENT STEAM 3.2 INDEX

Manufacturer	Plate No	SER No
Burnley Ironworks Co.	4	SER 980
George Saxon Ltd	1	SER 1134
J. Petrie	3	SER 698
R. Daglish & Co.	5	SER 794
R. J. Stringer	2	SER 1136
Robinson & Cook	6	SER 937

Stationary Steam Engines of Great Britain
The National Photographic Collection

THE VOLUMES:

1 Yorkshire

2 Scotland, Cumberland, Co Durham, & Northumberland

3 Lancashire (two books: Volume 3.1 & 3.2)

4 Wales, Cheshire, Shropshire

5 North Midlands: Derbyshire, Leicestershire, Lincolnshire, Nottinghamshire, Staffordshire

6 South Midlands: Berkshire, Bristol, Buckinghamshire, Gloucestershire, Herefordshire, Hertfordshire, Oxfordshire, Warwickshire, Worcestershire

7 The South and South West: Cornwall, Devon, Dorset, Hampshire, Isle of Wight, Somerset, Wiltshire

8 London & South East: London, Kent, Middlesex, Surrey, Sussex

9 East Anglia: Bedfordshire, Cambridgeshire, Essex, Norfolk, Northants, Suffolk

10 Marine engines

General Specification for all Volumes

Hardback, sewn binding with a laminated dust jacket. Printed on high quailty paper, size: 246 x 172mm (approx 9.75 x 6.75 inches).

Prices will vary according to length. Volume 1 is the longest book. On some of the smaller volumes, opportunity may be possible to incorporate additional photographs from George Watkins' field note books, which are additional to the main engine record and not generally available. Volume 3 (Lancashire) is split into two parts.

Hardback books on local history which you will enjoy
having and dipping into time and again.

Full details upon request

LANDMARK
Publishing Ltd ● ● ●

Waterloo House, 12 Compton, Ashbourne, Derbyshire DE6 1DA England
Tel 01335 347349 Fax 01335 347303
e-mail landmark@clara.net web site: www.landmarkpublishing.co.uk

LANDMARK COLLECTOR'S LIBRARY

LANDMARK COLLECTOR'S LIBRARY

STATIONARY STEAM ENGINES OF GREAT BRITAIN

THE NATIONAL PHOTOGRAPHIC COLLECTION

VOLUME 4: WALES, CHESHIRE & SHROPSHIRE

George Watkins

# ACKNOWLEDGEMENTS

Thanks are due to Keith Falconer who had the foresight to acquire the collection for the RCHME, and to Helga Lane, (late of the RCHME Salisbury office) who made the original computer database of the Steam Engine Record.

Much help in the production of these volumes has been given by David Birks, National Monuments Record Archives Administration Officer; Anna Eavis, Head of Enquiry and Research Services, and the members of the public search room staff at Swindon.

Colin Bowden, Brendan Chandler and Jane Woolrich did the often-difficult proof checking.

Many thanks to John Cornwell for providing the photographs of the author.